MW00812415

NEEM

Nature's Healing Gift to Humanity

Klaus Ferlow

NEEM
RESEARCH

DEAR MICHELLE!

LET'S CELEBRATE LIFE!

Klaus Ferlow

Neem - Nature's Healing Gift to Humanity

Copyright © 2015 by Klaus Ferlow

First edition 2015   Second Edition 2016

Library and Archives Canada Cataloguing in Publication

All rights reserved. No part of this publication may be reproduced, stored in a retrieval system, or transmitted in any form or by any means, electronic, mechanical, photocopying or otherwise, without the prior permission of the copyright owner. Applications for such permission, with a statement of the purpose and extent for the reproduction, should be addressed to the publisher.

Neem Research, PO Box 3197, Mission, B.C., V2V 4J4, Canada

http://www.neemresearch.ca   neemresearch1@gmail.com

ISBN 978-0-9937275-0-4

Although the author and publisher have made every effort to ensure that the information in this book was correct at press time, the author and publisher do not assume, and hereby disclaim, any liability to any party for any loss, damage, or disruption caused by errors or omissions, whether such errors or omissions result from negligence, accident, or any other cause.

The information is offered for its educational value only and should not be used in the diagnosis, treatment or prevention of disease. Any attempt to diagnose or treat illness should come under the direction of your health care provider.

Cover image courtesy of Dr Leo Rebello

This book is dedicated to Rose, my loving wife and partner for over 50 years. You have been my inspiration and motivation. Your encouragement, help, integrity, fortitude, love, companionship, intelligence and persistence have made this work possible. I thank you from the bottom of my heart.

Acknowledgments

I thank my wife, Rose, for supporting me while this book was taking shape, and I am grateful to my family for their love and support.

Thanks also to the following relatives, friends and business associates for inspiring me with fresh courage when I needed it, including my sister Elfie and brother-in-law Juergen Kirste, sister-in-law Hildegard Hausmann, and nephew Niels Hausmann.

A special thanks to my long-time friends: Ernst Heuft, Klaus Hoffman, Harald Bleier, Wolf Wilbert, Jeffrey Franckhauser, Luan and Jean Foo, Emmy Kennedy, Barrie Alden, Gerda Paulsen, Josephine Perkman, Horst Teutsch, Günter & Heidi Zschiesche, Resie Giesen and our good neighbors John and Connie Berghuis.

Thanks to my colleagues for believing in me: Praveen Jaipura, Neelam Toprani, Dr. Shekar Annambhotla, Professor Dr Ludwig Max Fischer, Eve Hillary ND MA, BHSc, Lorna Hancock BA, Conrad Richter, Dr. Carolyn Dean MD ND, Dr. Joaquim Morgado MD, Dr. Julia Christensen ND, Dr. Malte Hozzel, Scott Tips Esq., Jonathan Eisen, Katherine Smith, Dr. Sandra Goodman, Daleen Scotten, Dr. Neil McKinney ND, Dr. Zoltan Rona MD, Dr. Iva Lloyd ND, Dr. David Schleich, Dr. David Scotten ND, Carlo Billinger, Michael Volker, Dr. Brian Schaefer, Randy Gomm BSc., Richard DeSylva RH DNM, Julie Cheng and Michelle Hancock.

Thanks also to Susanne Garmsen, MA, C.Tran (DE-EN, FR-EN), Katherine Carroll NTP, Dr. Judy Nelson DC ND MH, Dr. Art Birzneck

DC, Armin Prahst MSc., Dr. Patricia Wolfe ND, Dr. Robert Van Horlick ND, Dr. Ray Lendvai ND, Elke and Stephan Krueger, Bernice Birzneck and Gunter Hartung.

Special thanks go to two world renowned entomologists, scientists and Neem experts: Professor Dr. Heinrich Schmutterer, formerly with the Institute for Phytopathology and Applied Zoology, Justus-Liebig University, Giessen, Germany, now retired, and Dr. Ramesh C. Saxena, Chairman of the Neem Foundation, Bombay (Mumbai), India. Thanks also to Mrs. Pramila Thakkar, one of the founding Trustees of the Neem Foundation, for her help and support.

This book is written for all who have suffered from health problems, particularly skin disorders. May this information help them and their health care providers, and may all beings on this planet be blessed by Neem's healing gifts.

Foreword

As a journalist and long-time analyst of the natural health industry, I have known of Klaus Ferlow since 1999. But it wasn't until some years later, after I'd corresponded with him about health care politics, that I understood the unique place that he occupied in the history of the modern botanical industry.

Klaus Ferlow was one of the first manufacturers to explore a trove of herbal treasures in exotic places, and to bring them to the Western consumer. His company, Ferlow Botanicals, was perfectly positioned to cater to the immense upsurge in consumer demand for non-toxic natural products and botanical medicines, long before others even recognized the trend.

His interest in Neem did not start as a commercial enterprise, but through an intensely personal journey with the botanical that possessed the power to heal him of a life-long condition. This life changing event came at a time when the plant was almost unheard of in the West.

As a manufacturer and master herbalist, Klaus remains uniquely qualified to share the healing power of Neem with those who want to know how this remarkable plant can help them.

Since Neem's versatility is almost unsurpassed among useful plants, its various components can be used as: a natural medicine, a multitude of household products, garden fertilizer, beauty aids, antiseptics, contraceptives and even as a non-toxic insect repellent.

Klaus has begun this book with his own personal story and his life changing experience with the Neem plant. In part two, he offers the reader a guide to using Neem for a large number of medicinal and household purposes. The final section contains the science and history of Neem and a comprehensive bibliography section that includes vast resources for both Neem enthusiasts as well as those in the Neem trade.

Apart from its entertaining and useful material, this book about Neem is also timely, appearing at the dawn of its world-wide development and debut onto the global scene.

We are about to see much more of the Neem plant in the years to come, and this book tells us the truly fascinating story of the tree that heals people and national economies alike.

Eve Hillary ND BHSc. MA
Sydney, Australia
July, 2015

Praise for the Book

Klaus Ferlow is a well-known and highly respected master herbalist from Canada. His recently published, remarkable new book, "Neem: Nature's Healing Gift to Humanity" is a true mine of valuable information about this unique plant, especially on the medical properties of the tree's ingredients. A lot of interesting old and new knowledge of Neem has been compiled in a attractive form, allowing the reader easy and effective utilization. K. Ferlow became a fan of Neem since he was cured of severe psoriasis using the extracts of this outstanding tree. Hopefully, this attractive new book will find a wide distribution and at the same time facilitate the use of Neem to the benefit of mankind.
--Professor Dr. H. Schmutterer, formerly with the Institute of Phytopathology & Applied Zoology, Justus-Liebig University, Giessen, Germany

Concise and well researched and documented book on Neem.
 -- Dr. Shekhar Annambothla, President , Association of Ayurvedic Practitioners of North America, Coppersburg, PA, USA.

This is an engaging, deeply personal account on one man's quest to bring the magic of Neem to the West. The Indian Neem tree has been welcomed across much of the world and now, through the efforts of Klaus Ferlow it is becoming better known in the Americas. One cannot help but be in awe of the power and versatility of Neem after reading this book.
--Conrad Richter, President, Richters Herbs, Goodwood, Ontario, Canada

Klaus Ferlow's life long passion for healing plants is evident in this wonderful book, allowing him to spread that love and help to many people as he testifies how much plants have helped him.
-- Carolyn Dean, M.D., N.D., Kihei, Hawaii, USA, The Doctor of the Future

Klaus Ferlow's well-researched and well-written book on the miraculous healing botanical Neem is more than just a good research and good reading, it can be life-saving. The practical health information found in this book is immediately useful to almost everyone. As Klaus shows us, Neem is the universal healer just as water is the universal solvent.
--Scott C. Tips, Esq., President & General Counsel of the National Health Federation, founded 1955, Monrovia, California, USA

Klaus Ferlow's book "Neem – Nature's Healing Gift to Humanity" is a great leap forward in highlighting the unique healing properties of the Neem tree, which originated in the Indian sub-continent, and has been used for treating various ailments for ages. Neem is unique in producing 100 highly valuable bio-active, synergistic chemicals, which are not only good for human health, but also for plant, animal, and environmental health. No wonder in 1992, the National Academy Press, Washington, D.C. Recognized this and published "Neem – A Tree For Solving Global Problems." Klaus's book highlights the unique healing properties of Neem products for various different ailments. The book is a must read! Today a variety of Neem products are available across the world, especially in the West for our benefits and better health.

--Dr. Ramesh C. Saxena, scientist, entomologist, Chairman of the Neem Foundation, Mumbai, India

Table of Contents

The Power of Herbs

*Herbs and plants are medical jewels gracing the woods and fields and lanes,
which few eyes see and few minds can understand.*

Carl von Linne Swedish Botanist & Naturalist

Image courtesy of Dr Leo Rebello

From the time I was a child, my life has been defined by a deep connection to herbs and Mother Earth. The reason for this lies in my cultural background and the unusual historical times that shaped my childhood. This can only be understood through my personal story.

I was born in 1938 in the once German region of East Prussia, which is today part of Poland and Russia. During and after the Second World War, millions of ethnic Germans were expelled from the region, which meant that my parents had to leave our home and belongings and flee to West Germany with me, my older brother and sister. Both sets of grandparents left at a different time and ended up in communist occupied East Germany where we could never see them again because of the Berlin wall that separated East from West Germany.

Even though we'd lost everything, we were still lucky to be alive, since over two million refugees were killed or starved to death on the long walk to freedom. We ended up in a small village in North Germany, one of countless refugee families who had to start over.

As a young boy, I often helped my family by picking Lily of the Valley, a fragrant cluster of white bell shaped flowers, which I sold in bunches to the local villagers for 10 pennies apiece. I was conscious of the fact that every little bit of income helped my family, and I still remember my mother telling me that I should always save up my money and buy the best quality that I could afford, 'since the bitterness of poor quality remains long after the sweetness of low price is forgotten'. Her sage advice would guide all my future purchases.

When I was older, I spent my spare time after school and on weekends working for local farmers during spring planting and summer harvest. Growing up in the German countryside meant that I was outdoors almost all year around and I quickly developed a deep love for Mother Nature, especially for herbs, vegetables, flowers, trees and shrubs.

My parents planted our own little garden and my mother educated us about the healing power of herbs and herbal remedies. In our family we used herbs in our daily diet, as well as for healing illnesses, since there was a doctor and medicine shortage after the war. My mother made delicious and fragrant homemade herbal products, including calendula cream. I remember some of my favorite herbal concoctions were elderberry juice with lemon and honey and garlic for colds.

My mother also picked herbs from the fields and forest and created tasty and healing tea blends. She made dandelion wine from the blossoms to strengthen the heart, and picked stinging nettles to make a cleansing tea. At home we also used peppermint, yarrow and chamomile tea on a regular basis. My mother continued this tradition well into her older years and we continued to enjoy her teas and potions all year round.

Herbs were such a large part of our culture that we even had lessons at school about the powerful medicinal value of herbs. I carried this knowledge into my adult life when I became a manufacturer of herbal products.

In our small village of 3600 souls we had only one medical doctor whose name was Dr Hans Wrede, but the villagers called him by his nick name, 'Hans go to bed', since he always advised bed rest for every ailment.

I never saw much of Dr Wrede, since I hardly ever had occasion to go to the doctor as a child. When I had a cold or fever, my mother gave me homemade elderberry juice and applied wet poultices to my throat, chest and sometimes even to my legs, and the fever was usually gone the next morning. I can't remember ever having a prescription drug when I was young.

From the time I was a child, I had witnessed the healing power of herbs so often that there was no doubt in my mind that natural medicine was effective and often miraculous in its ability to heal.

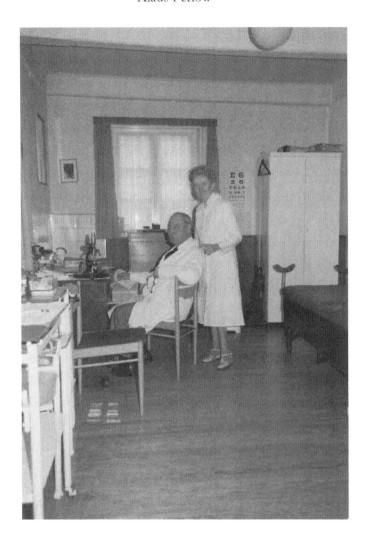

Dr Hans Wrede Sr. and wife. ('Dr Go-to-Bed')
Photo Courtesy of Dr Hans-Karl Wrede Jr.

When I was 17, I moved away from home to start an apprenticeship in sales and marketing. The large city, where I now found myself, was polluted by huge steel mills and other heavy industry.

From the stress of moving, the change in lifestyle, and the pollution, I soon developed a painful skin condition on my scalp and elbows which the doctor diagnosed as psoriasis. At times the flare ups were so bad that I could not get a comb through my hair due to the crust that covered my scalp. It was the beginning of many trips to the doctor and endless prescriptions which never seemed to get rid of the painful skin eruption. Worse still, for the first time, my mother's simple herbal remedies did not help either.

Forty years later I was to discover a super herb with astonishing healing properties, which had a miraculous effect on my psoriasis. But before I tell that story, I would like to take the reader on the path to its discovery.

As a young man just starting out in my sales career, I fell in love with a beautiful young woman, Rose, and decided that she was the one I wanted to spend the rest of my life with. Fortunately, she accepted my proposal, and after our marriage, we set out on our epic journey together, first into parenthood, when our two sons Peter and Harald were born, and later we migrated to Canada.

After a few tough years as new migrants in our adopted country and several jobs in sales and marketing, I took a risk and decided to open Ferlow Botanicals, my own manufacturing and distribution business of herbal medicinal and personal care products with no harmful, toxic, chemical ingredients.

Little did I know at the time that I was well ahead of the curve as one of the first manufacturers to offer non-toxic personal care products to an emerging market of environmentally aware consumers in North America.

The next years were good to us. Our two sons, Peter and Harald, were growing up, and business was expanding nicely. There was only one problem that refused to go away. The stubborn psoriasis that I'd developed as a teenager resisted all the pills and potions that doctors and herbalists had to offer. Fortunately, I was soon to discover a super herb with the power to heal almost anything.

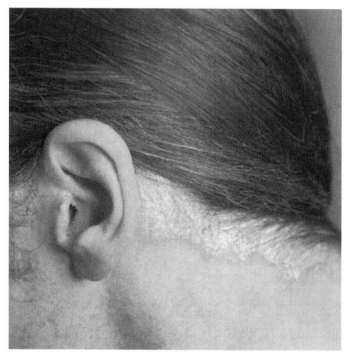

Typical scalp psoriasis in a young male

Finding the Billion Dollar Tree

It is health that is real wealth and not pieces of gold and silver.

Mahatma Gandhi

By 1994, my herbal products were selling well and various health groups were asking me to give talks all over Canada. Over the years, hundreds of people have come up to me afterwards to share their stories of the healing they had received from using the herbal products. I was amazed and delighted for them, but wished that I could say the same for my psoriasis, which had stubbornly refused to budge.

Just as I was beginning to wonder whether I was missing a key piece of information, I had the good fortune of tuning in to the Canadian Broadcasting Corporation which featured *The Nature of Things* with Dr David Suzuki, a program describing the miraculous healing power of the Neem tree from India, in a documentary called, *What's in a Neem?*

I wondered if Neem could help my skin condition and was determined to try it. But since Neem products were not yet on the market, and the raw extracts were hard to find, I had to formulate it myself with the help of a compounding chemist and a French supplier who provided the raw extract made of the Neem leaves.

Neem leaves and flowers

Once the first few batches of Neem cream were made, I trialled them on myself, and my wife massaged the cream into my scalp each day for 9 weeks. Initially, not much happened, but after the first few weeks my skin gradually cleared and healed over until I had brand new healthy skin where the flaky rash had been since my teenage years.

For the psoriasis on my elbows I rubbed a few drops of cold pressed Neem kernel oil into the patches each day. Since the oil has different healing properties compared to the leaf extract, I found that the rash on both elbows healed completely within 3 weeks. Since then, I have rubbed my elbows with one drop of Neem oil per week to prevent the rash recurring.

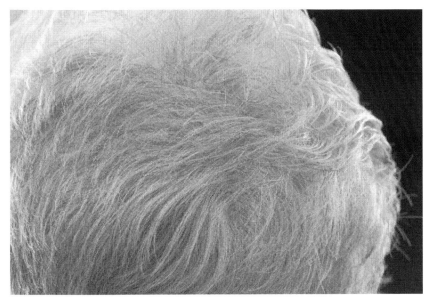

Healthy hair and scalp after using Neem cream

After such a miraculous result, I started researching Neem in the scientific literature and found plenty of evidence of Neem's efficacy.[1] Based on studies that supported the healing properties of Neem, I started to manufacture Neem cream and later a Neem oil blend, which sold well through holistic practitioners. Since developing those first two products, my two sons have joined Ferlow Botanicals and helped to develop additional Neem products such as shampoo, conditioner, soap, tincture and toothpaste.

By sheer luck, I had come across one of the greatest botanical treasures in the biosphere, the 'azadirachta indica' or 'the free tree of India'. This

---

[1] Pandey, S. S., Jha, A. K., & Kaur (1994). *Aqueous extract of neem leaves in treatment of Psoriasis vulgaris.* Indian Journal of Dermatology, Venereology, and Leprology, 60(2), 63.

adaptable tree offers over a thousand uses to humans, animals and the environment, including medicinal uses and its properties as a natural insect repellent and pesticide.

According to the National Research Council, Neem may eventually benefit every person on the planet, since no other tree offers as many by-products useful to humans. Indeed, as foreseen by some scientists, this plant may usher in a new era in non-toxic pest control and provide millions with inexpensive medicines and personal care products. Its birth control properties could be used to develop safe contraception options for couples, and its use in the environment could, in future, reduce erosion, deforestation, help to improve soil fertility and rehabilitate degraded wasteland.

The commercial applications of the Neem tree are so valuable that it is also called 'the billion dollar tree', but the healing I received from its leaves cost me only a few dollars and it was priceless and life altering.

After I was healed of a long-standing skin condition I wanted to tell the whole world about this miraculous plant. A few years later, this turned out to be exactly what happened. After developing Neem products and selling them throughout North America, their popularity soon put me into the spotlight. I was beginning to get a reputation for being one of the first manufacturers to bring Neem to the Western world.

Over the years, Neem had attracted the interest of many key people for a variety of reasons. Soon, I was to have the good fortune of meeting some of the most brilliant minds on the planet, when they all came together during one unforgettable week to discuss the Billion Dollar Neem tree.

The miraculous Neem tree, Azadirachta indica A. Juss

On the Neem Trail

Until man duplicates a blade of grass, nature can laugh at his so-called scientific knowledge. Remedies from chemicals will never stand in favor compared with the products of nature, the living cell of the plant, the final result of the rays of the sun, the mother of all life.

Thomas Edison

By 2012, I had manufactured Neem products for over 20 years and my fascination with it only grew stronger after hearing one success story after another from customers who had benefitted from this amazing plant.

During these years, I had also become well known in the botanical industry and developed many contacts, some of whom encouraged me to visit India from where the Neem tree originated. For many years I had dreamed of a chance to learn more about Neem, its propagation and cultural history. My chance came when I was invited to give a presentation at the 6th International World Neem Conference in Nagpur, India to talk about my own personal experience with psoriasis and Neem, a subject close to my heart.

Before I was due to leave, a few colleagues, who had already been to India, warned me to brace myself. They explained that the country is a fascinating mix of contradictions, steeped in a rich and ancient cultural history and offset by poverty that is at first shocking to Western eyes.

On a cold November day I boarded a 22 hour flight from my hometown, Vancouver Canada to Frankfurt Germany, where I had a short layover before flying on to Mumbai (formerly named Bombay) India.

I emerged from the airport into the steamy, chaotic city that 25 million people call home. The taxi ride through the streets of Mumbai was not for the faint of heart as the driver careened through the busy city teeming with a million people on foot, on motor bikes, mopeds and bicycles. I cringed as the driver narrowly missed a husband, wife and two kids piled on a tiny moped, and continued unfazed through oncoming traffic with horn blaring and without an inch to spare between vehicles.

Holy Cow in Indian city traffic

I braced myself in the back seat, and glanced out the window at the exotic sights. Among the sea of people, wandered homeless street dogs and cows that idly crossed the street, bringing the chaotic traffic to a stop from time to time. The driver reminded me that it is a jail-able offense to kill or injure a cow, which is considered holy in India.

On the way to the hotel we passed through the city's poverty stricken outer suburbs that are home to Mumbai's 6.5 million slum dwellers. I found it sad to see entire families living in makeshift dwellings, under tarps or metal sheets and without running water or toilets. Many of these families were selling street food from a small stand to make ends meet.

As we approached the central business district I saw increasing signs of affluence, until the driver dropped me at my hotel entrance. I paid him and was glad to arrive in one piece.

It was a relief to finally be in the cool and comfortable hotel room where I could have a long soak and a nap to take the edge off the culture shock and jet lag. Over the next few days I wanted to catch up with a few colleagues and be rested enough for some sightseeing around Mumbai before I had to catch a flight to Nagpur, about 850 km west of Mumbai, to attend the World Neem Conference.

The next day my colleagues and I enjoyed a lunch of spicy Indian fare and I listened with great interest to an Ayurvedic doctor who spoke at length about the ancient healing philosophy of India. Ayurveda is an ancient system of life (ayur) and science (veda) which originated in India over 5000 years ago. Its mind-body approach to healing evolved from the deep insights gleaned by the great rishis or seers of India who came to understand the fundamentals of creation and human health through the insight of meditation and other spiritual practices.

Ayurvedic medicine is the polar opposite of the Western medical model that almost exclusively uses drugs, surgery and chemotherapy to control symptoms of disease. Instead, Ayurveda focuses on a variety of different natural treatments that achieve a balance in the physical, mental, emotional and spiritual aspects of the person. Its ultimate aims are to assist the individual's quest towards a healthy and balanced lifestyle and toward emotional growth and self realization.

Ayurvedic diagnostic tools include checking the skin, eyes, tongue and ears thoroughly to ascertain the patient's general health. This is followed by pulse reading, which not only helps the doctor to determine the internal health of the patient, but is also said to form a spiritual connection between the doctor and the patient who both work together for the patient's healing. Unlike the Western intellectual, detached approach, Ayurveda credits healing to the supreme universal intelligence of consciousness that expresses itself through the body-mind-spirit of both the healer and the healed.

Another Ayurvedic tool is to determine the patient's dosha, or individual physical and mental constitution type. The types include Vata, Pitta and Kapha, and once established, the healer can individualize treatments for patients, since everyone responds to the same treatment in a different way.

Ayurvedic treatments include: diet, massage, yoga, meditation, surgery and various medicinal plants, essential oils and herbs accompany most of these treatments.

I was delighted to hear that Neem has deep roots within the Ayurvedic health system due to its versatility and miraculous healing powers. For centuries, the Neem tree has been called the village pharmacy, since its bark, leaves, roots and oil have been medicinally used to keep many diseases at bay, including: skin diseases, ulcers, gastro intestinal problems, mouth and gum disease, diabetes, dementia, high blood pressure and high cholesterol.

Though I had manufactured many Neem products over the years, I was eager to see and touch a Neem tree in its native environment. One of my colleagues offered to take me around the sights of Mumbai the next day and I gratefully accepted his offer but didn't think I would be seeing a Neem tree in the busy metropolis.

After saying goodbye to the group and returning to my hotel room, I thought about the incredible value of the Neem tree and the comfort and healing it must have brought to millions down through the ages and right up to the present day. While I was in India, I wanted to find out what I could do to help preserve this precious resource for future generations.

The next day my friend arrived and we set out on a sightseeing tour around Mumbai. There was no shortage of trains and three wheeler taxis willing to take us around the sights in stifling 38 C and 80% humidity.

We took a train and then a ferry across to Gharapuri, an island just offshore from the city, to visit Elephanta Caves where artisans had sculptured magnificent figures out of the rock walls inside the caves during the seventh century and dedicated their works to Shiva, one of the Hindu Deities.

On the way back from the sacred site, I was amazed to see a few graceful Neem tree specimens, their leaves giving shade and refuge to the throngs of people flowing like a river through the busy streets and alleys of

Mumbai. It is said in India that the Neem tree's shade is 2-3 degrees cooler than any other shade.

Noting my surprise, my guide reminded me that a Neem tree traditionally stood in the middle of each Indian village. It was, after all, the village pharmacy.

Neem tree in busy Indian city - the village pharmacy tradition

Neem on the Global Stage

The leaves of the trees shall be for the healing of the nations.

Revelation 22:2

The flight to Nagpur was so smooth that I was able to write some notes for the presentation I was scheduled to give at the 6th International World Neem Conference the next day. I felt butterflies in my stomach as I wondered who would be in the audience, since the conference, organized by the Neem Foundation, was attracting researchers, academics and experts from around the world to discuss how Neem could be used for the good of humanity. I'd wanted to attend this conference for a long time and now I was about to learn more about Neem and finally getting a chance to meet the larger than life personalities who were championing its cause and bringing it onto the global stage.

My first impression of Nagpur from the back seat of the taxi was a pleasant surprise. Unlike chaotic Mumbai, it seemed a livable city with its large population offset by leafy parks (with Neem trees, of course) and a good transportation network made for a greater sense of organization. The driver proudly told me that Nagpur was the centre of the Indian orange trade and that its inhabitants had the highest literacy rate (93%) in all of India. That didn't surprise me; the city was clearly a thriving business hub in central India.

After a short 15 minute ride from the airport, the driver dropped me off at the opulent Hotel Sun n Sand where I could relax and recharge in five star comfort. This afforded me a welcome break, since I was now getting more than a little nervous about my presentation the next day. At least I didn't have to travel anywhere to attend the conference, since it was being held in the hotel's conference room the following day, November 21, 2012.

The next morning I walked into the World Neem Conference and found myself among some illustrious company. Over 100 delegates had attended from industry, universities and research institutions around the world.

This extraordinary gathering was the work of the Neem Foundation chairman, Dr Ramesh Saxena, whose knowledge and standing in the scientific community as a Neem expert and entomologist drew the delegates together from every corner of the world. With the help of Mrs Pramila Thakkar, the managing trustee of the Neem Foundation, these delegates were now assembled in one room in a spirit of co-operation and looking to find ways of harnessing the Neem plant into service of humanity.

I felt fortunate to be part of such a truly worthwhile and positive global event. For several months I had wanted to thank both of them in person for inviting me to speak at the conference, but it would have to wait, since Dr Saxena was a busy host throughout the four day conference.

Once seated at my designated table I looked forward to kicking back and hearing the speakers, but was caught off guard when the MC called me up to the stage, since I was one of the first presenters on the first day of the conference.

Standing at the podium was daunting, but once I started sharing my own personal story of how Neem cured my psoriasis, I noticed, by the friendly and interested looks, that my presentation was well received by the other delegates.

The author presenting at the World Neem Conference

I was relieved to finish my talk and pleased to get my core message across: that this miraculous plant seems to have an intelligent ability to help the body to permanently heal itself, even from a long standing skin condition like psoriasis. Unlike the temporary symptomatic relief that pharmaceutical drugs might give, (although no such medications were effective for me), the experience of being totally healed of this condition by the Neem plant has been absolutely life changing for me.

I had barely settled back into my chair when a journalist team from National India Television arrived to conduct an interview with me and several other delegates who had also presented their talks that morning.

Somehow I managed to convey my message about Neem and the interview was due to be broadcast twice the next day on the English TV Channel.

That night, a conference dinner was hosted on the lawn of the Pride Hotel in Nagpur with mouth watering Indian food, drinks and entertainment. I had a chance to meet delegates who were working on unravelling the mystery of Neem and discovering its many useful properties. Some were scheduled to speak the next day and I couldn't wait to hear their presentations. Meanwhile, I found the delicious Indian cuisine and exotic dancers enchanting under the warm, night sky.

The second day started off with several world class speakers who presented information on Neem's development into anti cancer medications as well as remedies to treat and prevent a host of degenerative diseases. Another speaker spoke on Neem's development into natural pesticides and its applications for use in organic farming.

I was interested to hear Professor Binay Panda's presentation on how he had cracked the genetic code of Neem two years previously. He is currently working at GANIT Labs, Bangalore on isolating the compounds in Neem that can be used as medicines.

One of my favourite speakers was Dr Joaquim Morgado from Portugal who spoke of his humanitarian work using Neem to treat the three diseases endemic in Africa: malaria, sleeping sickness and filaria. Particularly interesting was his use of Neem oil in his own medical practice where he has successfully treated and completely healed patients with burns, psoriasis, bedsores and non-healing wounds, in record time.

Dr Morgado's altruism was clearly evident when he mentioned that, unlike the pharmaceutical industry, which patents compounds isolated from

Neem for profit, he was using the freely available natural Neem product 'for the good of humanity' and to 'alleviate suffering'. On hearing this I felt like shaking the man's hand and thanking him for all he had done to make the world a better place. In fact, I got a chance to do this after the conference where I also found out that Dr Morgado was planning to cultivate 20 000 hectares of Neem in Mozambique to produce Neem oil on a large scale for medicinal use. We have been in close contact ever since the conference.

Dr Joaquim Morgado

Finally, I was fascinated to hear Dr Pasquale Mosesso from Italy, who is researching the anti cancer properties of Neem. His early work is already showing that certain Neem compounds are able to arrest cell division in tumours without damaging the surrounding normal cells. This means that the Neem plant could, one day, provide cancer patients with a relatively non-toxic cancer treatment, compared to standard chemotherapy, which is associated with severe side effects.

On the third day, the group went on an excursion to the Neem Research Development Technology Centre in the nearby village of Gondkhairy, north of Nagpur.

There, we received a fascinating tutorial on how Neem materials are extracted from the various parts of the plant and I was finally able to get close enough to hug a Neem tree.

A knowledgeable guide showed us the fresh components of the tree, including Neem flowers and seeds.

Neem Research Development Technology Centre (Image courtesy of Dr Leo Rebello)

Neem flower

Neem fruit

During the lectures and workshops I learnt about Neem cake, the by-product obtained after cold pressing the Neem tree fruits and kernels.

This dark brown organic material is sold and used as fertilizer which offers a bonus to gardeners and farmers, since it is pest repellent.

I also learnt about the different varieties of harvested Neem materials and was able to collect samples of Neem bark and powder, Neem cake powder, Neem dried fruits, kernels and seeds.

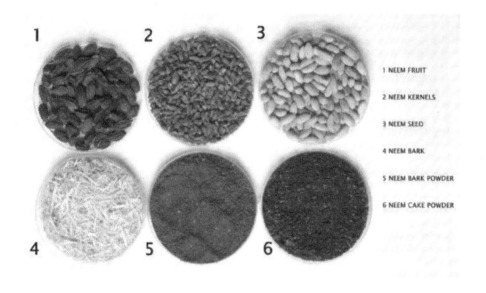

1 NEEM FRUIT

2 NEEM KERNELS

3 NEEM SEED

4 NEEM BARK

5 NEEM BARK POWDER

6 NEEM CAKE POWDER

Neem plant raw materials (image by C.Berghuis)

At the workshop I was also lucky enough to catch up with Dr Saxena and spoke with him at some length about his involvement with Neem. For the past four days he had been the heart and soul of the conference and the key note speaker, as well as conference host. As the chairman of the Neem

Foundation for the past 22 years, his tireless efforts in bringing together researchers, industry and Neem experts has formed the core of the Neem global movement.

Dr Saxena spoke freely about Neem as he generously posed with me for a picture near a large field of turmeric plants. His passion for saving the environment was clearly evident.

Dr. R.C Saxena, Chairman, Neem Foundation, Klaus Ferlow
in the Turmeric Field of the Neem Research Foundation's Farm in Nagpur on 23/11/2012
during the World Neem Conference visit to India.

(Original image courtesy of Dr Leo Rebello)

He told me that: 'killing and destruction of insect pests with toxic insecticides is outdated if they can be otherwise incapacitated or neutralized with materials such as Neem. Neem not only repels pests, but reduces feeding, reduces growth and development, minimizes fertility, and reduces hatching of their eggs. Surprisingly, the pests' natural enemies (parasites and predators), which are the very basis of biological control, are not affected by application of Neem. This is truly a non-violent, Gandhian approach to sustainable pest management!'

Dr Saxena's philosophy deeply resonated with mine, since I liked the idea of a natural substance that killed pests but left the rest of the food chain intact.

I was curious about what first attracted Dr Saxena to study Neem and how it led him to become a world authority on it. I was aware that, as an entomologist, he had authored many academic papers on the subject.[2] He had also collaborated with the renowned Neem expert Professor Dr Heinrich Schmutterer and contributed to the definitive academic text, 'The Neem Tree', edited by the Professor who is considered the father of modern Neem.[3]

During the 1950s, Professor Dr Schmutterer had travelled to the Sudan as a young scientist studying entomology and plant biology, only to encounter a locust plague. Fortunately, he noticed that the Neem trees were the only ones to remain green, healthy and virtually untouched by the locusts, which proved to be a discovery that started the research into Neem as a pesticide

---

[2] Two of Dr Saxena's papers are published in this book, with his permission. One appears under the chapter heading: *The Neem Tree – A Study.*
[3] Prof. Dr. Heinrich Schmutterer is also a contributor to the book, *Neem: A tree for solving global problems*, National Academy Press, 1992.

and medicinal plant. He is credited as being the first scientist to put Neem on the map for research and development.

Over many years, the Professor and Dr Saxena enjoyed a fruitful collaboration and a close friendship, and both developed a reputation for being the leading experts on Neem.

I would have enjoyed meeting Professor Dr Schmutterer at the conference but that was not to be. Dr Saxena explained that the elder academic could not attend due to some health issues and added that he will be celebrating his 90th birthday in April.

Fortunately, since then I was able to speak at length on the phone with Prof. Dr Schmutterer on June 30, 2014, and again on March 3, 2015, and he was very kind to encourage me to write and finish this book. In the last phone conversation he agreed to a personal meeting in August 2015 in Germany, and I have now returned from this trip after having had the rare opportunity of sitting down and talking with this extraordinary man.

Having a chance to meet this living legend made me realise how fortunate it was that in past years Professor Dr Schmutterer had been a regular speaker at previous Neem conferences where he had shared his vast knowledge with the world.

Professor Dr Heinrich Schmutterer at previous Neem Conference, 2002

In any case, I was honoured and delighted to finally get the chance to chat with Dr Saxena and to thank him and Mrs Thakkar, in person, for inviting me to speak at the conference.

Dr Saxena and Mrs Thakkar

After meeting the committee on the last day, I packed my suitcase and left India knowing that my long time passion for all things Neem had been completely vindicated.

On the long flight home to wintry Vancouver, I knew in my heart that this was indeed the tree that could heal the nations of the earth.

The Tree That Heals Nations

Every man is a creature of the age in which he lives;
only a few are able to raise themselves above
the ideas of the time.

Voltaire

When I was desperately searching for a psoriasis remedy back in the 1990s, Elke and Stephan Krueger, a couple living in Hanover Germany, were in the identical position. Though we did not know each other at the time, our introduction to Neem was a turning point in our lives.

In the mid 1990s, Elke and Stephan ran a consulting and import business for environmentally friendly products which included health products from India and other countries. At the time, three serious skin conditions, eczema, psoriasis and dyshidrosis, were making Elke's life a misery. Worse still, her eldest child also suffered from neurodermatitis, a painful and itchy skin condition. Elke wondered if any of the health products that she and Stephan were importing could help.

At first Elke experimented with Neem products, but they only made her skin condition worse. Few, if any, ingredients were listed on labels in those days, but after some research, Elke discovered that these products contained additives and preservatives such as formaldehyde, methyldibromo glutaronitrile and imidazolidinyl urea.

Suspecting these chemicals were responsible for inflaming her skin rather than the Neem, Elke tried the remedy again after sourcing pure Neem products. When her skin condition miraculously improved she knew her theory had been correct and she then used the Neem on her eldest child with good effect. Within a short time Elke and her child experienced accelerated healing until their skin and nails were restored to a supple, healthy state that they had not known before the pure Neem oil applications.

Elke Krueger in her Bio Drogerie

After experiencing the phenomenal natural healing power of Neem, Elke and Stephan were inspired to start their own business selling natural goods in their hometown of Hanover. They called their store PUR – Bio Drogerie, which included an organic apothecary stocked with various natural cosmetic, toiletry and medicinal products, many of which were made from Neem.

In the years that followed, Elke and Stephan travelled extensively in search of raw materials for their organic products business, which took them to parts of the world that had become a desert due to over farming and corporate overexploitation.

Feeling devastated about the loss of farmlands and productivity that led to mass migration of people into overcrowded cities, they wanted to help the people and restore their land to its former productive and prosperous state. This inspired them to found Plan Verde (Green Plan), a non-profit organization dedicated to planting trees to rehabilitate the soil, restore productivity and reestablish local economies. It was an ambitious plan and at the time they hardly knew where to start since they were only two people on a shoestring budget.

Elke and Stephan chose Peru to focus their Plan Verde's efforts on, since its coastal areas had lost their native tropical forests after its growing population had too heavily relied on the land for timber and farming. They decided on Piura, a sprawling town near the Ecuadorian border which had its outskirts turned into a desert that the farmers were no longer able to cultivate. The entire region, they believed, had been overexploited, abandoned and forgotten by the rest of the world.

Since many local people had already abandoned the area to look for work in even larger cities such as Lima, the couple wanted to attract them back to the region to regain their land, pride and prosperity.

After months of research on how this impossible task could be achieved, Elke and Stephan discovered that none other than the Neem tree would be capable of restoring Piura's economy, since it could provide the local people with a natural resource that grew rapidly, provided shade, restored the soil, warded off insect pests and produced a variety natural medicines and useful products from its biomass. As much as their idea sounded feasible in theory, they both knew it would soon be time to roll up their sleeves and put their objectives into practice.

Around 2006, the couple abandoned their comfortable home and lifestyle in Germany and moved to Piura. Their first major challenge was to actually find a Neem tree, and if they couldn't locate one, since it was not native to South America, they would have to be the first to introduce the tree to the region, an almost impossible task since it was illegal to import seeds into Peru.

Finding an existing Neem tree in Peru proved harder than originally thought, until they heard about a civil engineer, Victor Zapata, who ten years earlier had received some Neem seeds from a visitor from India. They were told that he had planted those two Neem seeds in his garden.

Elke and Stephan set out to try and locate the house on the outskirts of Piura. Once they had found the neighborhood they noticed one house that stood out from all the others. They knew they were on to something when they saw two enormous shade trees in the otherwise barren neighborhood.

The Kruegers knocked on the door and a woman greeted them with the customary Peruvian hospitality. They soon discovered that they had arrived there a few months too late. The civil engineer turned out to be her husband, but unfortunately he had died not long before. The good news was that those were indeed two Neem trees growing majestically in the garden, although they were standing in puddles after some water pipes had burst.

Two giant Neem trees in front of the Zapata's house

After explaining their mission to Mrs Zapata, Elke and Stephan were given permission to gather seeds from the trees in front of the house. Mrs Zapata had become very emotional about the Krueger's surprise arrival. Apparently, it had been her husband's dream to cultivate the trees, but he hadn't lived to see it. Now these strangers, who came all the way from Germany, would make this dream into a reality.

Elke wasted no time in starting the seed collection. She recalls the neighbours' fascination as they watched her digging out the precious seeds from the sandy soil and picking them out of mud and dog excrement from around the trees. To Elke, this was a labour of love since she firmly believed that: 'The trees are the foundation for the development of a culture'.

Elke collecting seeds from the Zapata Neem trees

Fortunately, both hardy Neem trees had survived getting their feet wet, while Elke and Stephan were able to rescue almost all the small seeds and seedlings that had sprouted in the puddles.

The Kruegers' hard work, the sturdy Neem tree and the generosity of Mrs Zapata, led to gathering the original seed stock of 25 000 that started off the Neem Pilot Project in Piura, Peru through Plan Verde e.V (the Krueger's registered non-profit organization).

The next question that occupied Elke and Stephan was whether their project had the support of the local community. Soon they received this message from a farm worker not far from Piura:

'My name is **Hermes Montoya**. *I am working on a mango plantation in the north of Peru and would like to tell you about the situation in our country.*

You come from Germany and our two countries are thousands of miles away from each other. But we have several things in common. We inhabit the same planet, and therefore we have the same dignity and responsibility for it. Peru had for a long time its own culture and history – **as an example Machu Picchu, the lost Inca City**. *It has been terminated by the Spanish conquerors. The colonial powers prevented that we could continue and develop our own way of life.*

Peru is a country with endless natural beauty and pride. However, vast areas of our country are used by huge powerful foreign international fruit corporations **and they have changed and even destroyed our nature, but also our lifestyle**. *Promises made by them for a better life for us through earning good money, building new roads, department stores etc. have not reached us nor materialized and we have lost much of our land and rights too!* **The fruit companies dictate our lives**. *We must take care of the fruits, plant and maintain and harvest them. For each 20 kg mango box the companies get paid Euro 3.50, from this only a very small portion reaches us farm laborers and we earn Euro 150.00 per month. This is just enough to pay for groceries, buy some clothes for our children or to ride with the bus. It is not enough to save any money and what happens if someone gets sick? The cost of living in Peru is very expensive!*

Cleaning-up rivers, reforest the woods, protect animals, everything is okay, **but it is even more important to be able going our own way again and gaining the right to our own development the way how we see it**. *We would like that our children have a life with dignity, health and freedom. We need projects that guarantee us* *a good income and that we can get away from the dependence and become responsible for our own life. I told you that because* **I want to teach the civilized countries what our situation is like here, and I hope they will help us to recover what belongs to us. I hope your idea and your project Plan Verde will contribute a bit towards that'.**

Thank you,
Hermes Montoya

Hermes Montoya

After receiving this heartfelt message, Elke and Stephan were certain that their project was both needed and welcomed by the local people, which

44

inspired them with the confidence to move forward with it. But despite their full commitment, the project posed a serious personal financial risk, since they had applied for funds and grants from many organizations and had been refused. They were now completely out on a limb, using their own resources.

Without any outside financial support, Elke and Stephan had to come up with cost saving shortcuts if they were going to succeed. They were up against high stakes with the 25 000 seedlings they had planted, and they counted on the fast growth of the Neem tree to bring the necessary return for the local community before they ran out of funds.

Elke with Neem seedlings and Plan Verde supporter, Dr Philine Oft, on left.

The fast growing Neem tree is known for rapidly halting erosion and restoring fertility to the soil and within 3-5 years it yields fruit and valuable plant based materials. To accelerate this process, Elke and Stephan invented an organic soil activator and fertilizer (EMKO EM 10) with beneficial soil microorganisms which has caused the trees to grow even more robustly and to bear fruit within 1½ years.

Since 2009, Elke and Stephan have worked miracles on a shoe string budget. In a few short years they have planted over 200 000 Neem trees and set up tree schools that teach local people how to manage the trees and their natural products.

They have also helped locals to establish other beneficial species including Moringa trees, vetiver grass and alfalfa to the area, which in turn has restored hope and prosperity to the region.

In 2012, the Kruegers met with Luis and Carmen Valencia, the directors of the Hogar de Cristo Piura orphanage, who do their best to raise orphans and homeless street children from the Piura area on inadequate funds from the government. They struggled daily to provide the children with a diet consisting mainly of rice, beans, and sweet rolls. The four goats on the property provide milk and meat and sometimes feed on the children's old school notebooks if food is scarce.

The Kruegers, along with the Valencias, set up a joint project to show the children how to maintain a clean water supply. They are presently planting Moringa and Neem trees to recondition the soil and cleanse the water supply around the grounds of the orphanage. They have also helped the children set up their own vegetable garden and chicken coop.

The children clearly enjoy the project which has restored their hope and purpose and provided the orphanage with the means to grow its own food.

Since then, Luis and Carmen have had a constant source of fresh food on the table and the satisfaction of knowing that their 14 orphaned children are developing new life skills and deriving satisfaction and meaning from their lives.

Hogar de Cristo Orphanage. Elke putting smiles on young faces with Neem seedlings

Stephan showing a young boy how to plant Neem tree

From left Luis and Carmen Valencia, Elke and Stephan Krueger and children

Elke and Stephan have enjoyed watching Piuran families become actively involved with the Plan Verde project and look forward to the time when the community fully establishes the production of Neem and Moringa oil, Neem soaps and other Neem products, which will create a better future for both the environment and the people of the area.

Over the years I have been touched and inspired by the Krueger's project. It's been an example of what can be done when the heart is in the right place. They gave an entire community hope for the future and asked nothing in return. This shows extraordinary character and courage. Their only motto was helping the Peruvians to help themselves, which in my view makes Neem Pilot Project, Piura, Peru a project with a heart.

I am a proud supporter of the Kruegers and ask that you also consider donating to their project.

To support the efforts of Stephan and Elke Krueger, please go to their website. Any amount of support is more than welcome:

http://www.plan-verde.org   or   http://www.plan-verde.com

Part 2

The Art of healing comes from nature and not from physicians.
Therefore, the physician must start from nature
with an open mind.

Paracelus

SHORT HISTORY OF HERBS

Herbs have been used since the first humans walked the earth, as food, medicine and for religious rites. They were first used by shamans of ancient indigenous cultures throughout Africa, Eurasia, Australia and the Americas.

Some of these prehistoric practices were passed down the generations through the spoken word, ritual and song, which built the early foundation of our modern herbal knowledge.[4]

Centuries later, during ancient Greek, Roman and Egyptian civilizations, herbal knowledge was written down on clay tablets and scrolls. References to the use of plants as medicine can be found written in Egyptian papyrus writings as early 3000 BC and are often referred to in the Bible:

Behold, I have given you every herb bearing seed, which is on the face of all the earth, and every tree, in which is the fruit of a tree yielding seed; to you it shall be for meat. (Genesis 1:29)

He causeth the grass to grow for the cattle, and the herb for the service of man. (Psalm 204:14)

Western herbal tradition has been passed down to the Western culture since the Middle Ages by the monks in Europe who grew herbs in their monasteries and used them as food, flavorings and medicines. In Germany, abbess and herbalist, Hildegard of Bingen, treated the sick with herbs.

Just a few examples of herbs in common use during past centuries includes, vinegar and myrrh, used as an antiseptic, while yarrow was used to treat headaches and battle wounds. Rose, lavender, sage and bay were used as much needed air fresheners during the plague years. The powerful opium poppy was introduced to Europe by Paracelsus in 1527 when its latex was made into a medicinal tincture and used to relieve the severe pain of surgery, disease and battle injuries.

---

[4] History of Herbal Medicine - About Us |. (n.d.). Retrieved from http://today-medicine.com/about-us

During English colonization, settlers took the herbs they used with them to America, Australia, Canada, New Zealand and Africa. Once colonists were settled in the new lands, they also adopted the herbal knowledge of the native indigenous cultures and sent them back to England and other parts of the world. In Britain, in the mid 1750s, Nicholas Culpeper published a famous book on how to make herbal elixirs and personal care products for people who wanted to make their own remedies instead of paying a doctor, chemist or herbalist.

HERBS AS FOOD

Herbs used for food are known as culinary herbs, and are added in small amounts to meats, vegetables or salads to add flavor, color or garnish to food, rather than as a main dish. In the past, herbs were only classed as the leafy parts of the plant, but in recent years, herbs and spices have merged to include the aromatic bark, roots or buds of plants such as cinnamon and clove.

According to the American Spice Trade Association, today spices have become known as; 'any dried plant product used primarily for seasoning purposes'. This all-inclusive definition seems to cover a wide range of plants like herbs, spice seeds and even dehydrated vegetables and spice blends. [5]

Culinary herbs and spices can come from the flowers, bark, leaves, and seeds, found on grasses, shrubs or trees. Leafy herbs include, rosemary, bay laurel leaves, or leaves from perennial shrubs such as mint, thyme, lavender or parsley. Some herbs derived from seeds include fennel, dill and celery seeds

---

[5] http://www.infoplease.com/askeds/difference-herb-spice.html

and peppercorns, while those derived from roots include, ginger and horseradish. Many culinary herbs, such as mint and garlic, also have medicinal properties as a stomach soother and immune booster.

SACRED HERBS USED FOR RELIGION OR SPIRITUALITY

Frankincense is a resin that comes from the Boswellia species of trees. It has long been a part of religious rites and is still used in Christian, Jewish and Muslim ritual.

In contrast, indigenous cultures often use a class of psychoactive plants and herbs known as entheogens for spiritual rituals. These powerful herbs are capable of altering consciousness and are still traditionally used by shamans to open the doors of mental awareness. One example is the Kava plant used by South Pacific cultures for medicinal, social and religious purposes, to induce relaxation, inspiration and a sense of wellbeing.

Another entheogen comes from the Ayahuasca vine. When used by Amazonian tribes of South America in a ceremonial setting, the plant can produce profound mental and spiritual insights. These herbs are so powerful that they are potentially dangerous in untrained hands, or when ingested by persons taking certain antidepressant medications, and their use is banned in many countries.

HERBS USED AS MEDICINE

Hundreds of herbs have been scientifically shown to be effective as herbal medicine since they are able to produce a variety of chemical compounds that can regulate biological functions in humans and promote beneficial health effects and healing. Some herbs, such as Wormwood, are also able to produce metabolites that can kill parasites in humans. The following is a short list of plants which have been traditionally used and can be effective in healing a variety of medical conditions when used as herbal medicine, either alone or in conjunction with standard medical treatments. [6]

- Alfalfa is used to lower cholesterol, as well as for urinary tract ailments and rheumatoid arthritis.
- Aloe Vera leaves are widely used to heal burns, lacerations, incisions and other wounds.
- Arnica is used as an anti-inflammatory for strains and bruises and for the relief of osteoarthritis.
- Astragalus is used in traditional Chinese medicine to strengthen the immune system, and is being investigated for its anti-aging and anti cancer properties.
- Black cohosh (Actaea racemosa) has historically been used for malaise, pain, as a diuretic and conditions related to menopause and menstruation.
- Clove (Syzygium aromaticum) is used for upset stomach and the oil is used to treat toothache.
- Cranberry (Vaccinium macrocarpon) used to alleviate problems related to the urinary tract.
- Evening primrose oil is used to treat skin disorders such as eczema, psoriasis, acne and inflammatory conditions such as rheumatoid arthritis.
- Ginkgo (Ginkgo biloba) leaf extract has been used to treat memory problems such as in Alzheimer's disease, fatigue, and tinnitus.

---

[6] American Botanical Council http://www.herbmed.org/

- Licorice root (Glycyrrhiza glabra) is used to treat stomach ailments, bronchitis and sore throat. It boosts natural interferon which makes it an effective treatment for viral illness and hepatitis.
- Marigold (Calendula officinalis) known as calendula, is most commonly used as a cream to treat skin wounds and inflammation.
- Milk thistle (Silybum marianum) is used to treat liver problems, type 2 diabetes and as a cholesterol lowering agent.
- Neem (Azadirachta indica) one of the most versatile herbs used to treat skin conditions, infections, fevers and burns, among many other conditions.
- Echinacea (Echinacea purpurea) and other species of Echinacea are used to alleviate symptoms of cold and flu.
- Sage (Salvia officinalis) is used to improve memory and cognitive function in patients with Alzheimer's disease.
- Thyme (Thymus vulgaris) is used to treat respiratory conditions such as bronchitis and colds.
- Turmeric (Curcuma longa) used in Ayurvedic and traditional Chinese medicine to aid digestion and liver function and as an anti-inflammatory to relieve arthritis pain.
- Valerian (Valeriana officinalis) has long been used to aid sleep and relaxation.

Beauty Is Skin Deep

Taking joy in living and an interest in good health is the best cosmetic.

Anon

Skin is the largest organ of our body forming our natural, attractive and versatile cover. It contains millions of nerve endings that perform a variety of important functions, including conducting signals from outside, like heat, cold, touch, pain and pleasure.

Intact skin also forms a barrier against harmful light and other rays, chemical substances, viruses and bacteria, heat and cold, and it cushions against blows, pressure and friction. It is a storage receptacle for fat, water and essential nutrients, and it maintains our constant body temperature through perspiration and the constriction and dilatation of pores. Obviously, skin is a mirror of human physical, emotional and spiritual balance and it openly displays an individual's state of health and lifestyle. There is no hiding, your skin reveals a lot about you to the world!

If skin is pale, loose, dry, spotty, or tired looking, a change in lifestyle is often the solution. Such changes may need to include; improving nutrition, staying away from junk food and pop drinks, artificial sweetener, smoking or excess alcohol and increasing whole foods in your diet, exercise and sleep and reducing stress. You can also achieve a balanced lifestyle through yoga, Pilates, meditation or all of the above.

If a polluted environment overloads the detoxifying organs such as the liver and gallbladder, the skin has to pick up the extra work to eliminate toxins from the body. This overload can lead to; dry skin conditions such as rashes, dermatitis, acne or eczema. To prevent chemical overload, avoid hazardous toxic chemicals in household and garden goods.

Our skin consists of three layers:

THE LAYERS OF HUMAN SKIN

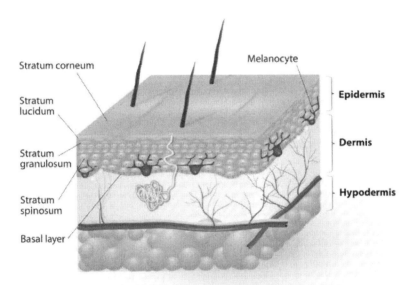

- The Epidermis - the top layer of the skin, which locks in moisture and blocks harmful substances from entering the body.
- The Dermis - the second layer of the skin, where the stretch marks occur, is where collagen and elastin fibers are produced which gives the skin the ability to resume its shape after stretching. More collagen means a firmer and younger appearance. It also contains

sweat and oil glands that lubricate skin, excrete toxins and regulate body temperature.

- The Hypodermis - the third layer of the skin which is composed of fat, connective tissue and blood vessels that carry off the waste and replenish skin cells.

SECRETS TO KEEPING YOUR SKIN HEALTHY

Moisturize: To keep the skin's natural protective barrier intact, use a non-irritating moisturizer like a Neem cream or natural lotion. Apply right after your bath or shower, when the skin is still damp, and reapply multiple times during the day as necessary, especially if using chlorinated water which will dry out your skin.

Avoid irritants: Common chemical irritants such as harsh soaps and cosmetics, cleaning products and chemicals in the workplace can cause itchiness and redness, and result in dermatitis or eczema. Ensure you are using natural and safe personal care and cleaning products and that your home and work environments are non toxic.

Showering and bathing: Avoid excessive bathing or showering in hot water with harsh soaps, since it will remove the protective oils from your skin and dry it out. Lukewarm water and a Neem soap would be ideal, or a mild bath product that is pH balanced and without harmful chemical ingredients.

Healthy diet: Avoid junk food, pop drinks, smoking, excess alcohol and caffeinated drinks and increase vitamin and antioxidant rich foods such as vegetables and fruits.

Water and sun: Stay hydrated with pure chlorine-free water. Detoxify with natural herbal remedies and expose your skin to some natural sunlight each day for vitamin D, while avoiding damaging overexposure to the sun or tanning salons.

Climate control: Keeping humidity a constant 55% at home with a humidifier, particularly in late fall and winter with the heating on, helps keep skin moist. This can be measured using a hydrometer, available at most hardware stores. Best room temperature would be 22 C (70 F). This helps prevent premature aging. [7]

---

[7] Further information on the National Skin Care Institute website:
http://www.skincarenet.org

GUIDE TO USING NEEM

Neem has been scientifically shown to be effective in healing skin and other conditions, and it has been safely used in Ayurvedic medicine for over two thousand years.

Topical Neem has been shown to be safe for use on adults, children and pets when used as directed. There have been no known adult fatalities associated with the medicinal use of Neem products, but there are just a few important rules for you to remember on how to use Neem safely and effectively.

- Use oral and topical Neem products as directed.
- Never ingest Neem oil orally.
- Do not give oral Neem capsules or oil to infants.
- Do not take Neem systemically if you intend to conceive a child, as it may act as a mild contraceptive.[8]
- Do not use if you are allergic to Neem.

When necessary, consult a health practitioner with experience in natural medicine for guidance.

---

[8] Kumar, S. Jattan, S (1995). *Neem-a green contraceptive.* Indian Forester,121(11),1006-1008.

When diet is wrong, medicine is of no use, when diet is correct, medicine is of no need.

Proverb

NEEM FOR COMMON SKIN DISORDERS

Acne/Pimples

The most common skin problems for people worldwide are acne and pimples, appearing on the face, back, neck, chest or shoulders. Causes include increased hormone production during puberty, poor diet, skin parasites and fungal infections, oily skin and a toxic lifestyle.

Research has shown that early teens are not the only group with acne, 81% of acne sufferers are aged between 15 – 44 years. If you find yourself over 30 and battling breakouts, don't despair. Most acne is associated with overactive oil glands in your skin and Neem offers a simple and effective remedy for each of the various types of pimples that appear below:

- **Whiteheads** – small white bumps under the skin.
- **Blackheads** – clearly visible black plugs in the pores appearing on the surface of the skin. They are usually resistant to scrubbing.
- **Papules** – small pink bumps visible on the skin surface.
- **Pustules** – clearly visible on the skin surface, they are red and inflamed with pus forming at the top.

Suggestions: Studies show that Neem effectively reduces the inflammation from clogged pores and kills the bacteria that cause acne.[9] To prevent or heal acne, first wash with Neem soap, then use a Neem cream or lotion to nourish and moisturize the skin.

For severe cases in adults or teens, external Neem application can be combined with oral use of the Neem tincture or Neem capsules as directed, which acts as an immune stimulant and body detoxifier as well as an anti bacterial agent.

Additionally, you can brew Neem tea from the leaves and also drop a few Neem leaves into your bathwater. Try to be patient though, since it may take some time before you see some improvements.

Dandruff

Nearly 50% of Westerners suffer from dandruff, which is characterized by itching and dry, flaky skin being cast off from the scalp. Though its exact cause is unknown, it is sometimes confused with yeast or fungal infections of the scalp, as well as seborrheic dermatitis caused by oily, irritated skin. Cradle cap is a related condition common in infants.

Suggestions: As with other forms of dermatitis, Neem has been found effective against dandruff as both an anti-inflammatory and anti-fungal preparation.[10] When used as a soap or shampoo, Neem will soothe the scalp, remove flaky skin and get rid of any fungus or yeast on the scalp.

---

[9] Brahmachari, G. (2004) *Neem—an omnipotent plant: a retrospection.*.Chembiochem, 5(4), 408-421.

[10] Dhamane, S., Asnani, G. et al. (2012). *Development and evaluation of herbal anti-dandruff hair gel.* World J Pharmacy Pharm Sci, 1(3), 1173-79.

In stubborn cases, adults and teens can also take Neem internally in the form of Neem tincture, tea or capsules, as directed. Regular application of Neem can also help to prevent dandruff.

Cradle cap in infants can be treated by using a gentle Neem baby soap or lotion on the scalp, as directed.

Eczema

Eczema is a non-contagious skin condition that can present in several different forms, but the most common include: 1. Atopic (an inherited type in children). 2. Contact (caused by a chemical irritant). 3. Seborrhoeic (affects the scalp, face and torso). 4. Dyshidrotic (blisters hands and feet).

Eczema generally causes inflammation resulting in scaly patches of red, cracked and painful skin. Over time the microscopic cracks and fissures can allow bacteria, viruses, and fungi into the skin to set up a secondary infection. The severity of this disease can vary; in mild forms the skin is dry, hot and itchy. More severe forms involve weeping blisters where the skin becomes broken, raw, bleeding and crusty.

Some contributory factors include: genetics, emotional stress, dietary insufficiency of omega fatty acids[11] and chemical exposure to harsh chemical products or chlorinated water.

Suggestions: Avoid harsh chemicals; try adding omega fatty acid supplements to diet and Himalayan salt or sea salt to bathwater.

---

[11] Horrobin, D. F. (2000). *Essential fatty acid metabolism and its modification in atopic eczema.* The American journal of clinical nutrition, *71*(1), 367s-372s.

Neem has been found effective in the treatment of eczema.[12] The condition can be treated topically with Neem shampoo, cream or lotion, soap, and systemically (in adults) with Neem tincture, tea or capsules, as previously outlined.

For the treatment of adult eczema, it is best to first use the Neem oil on the affected area for a few days, followed by the Neem lotion or cream to relieve the intense itching and redness of eczema. Wash the affected area with Neem soap or shampoo. In severe cases adults can supplement by drinking Neem leaf tea twice daily or taking a course of Neem capsules as directed. For extra topical relief, grind Neem leaves and turmeric together with a mortar and pestle and apply topically to the rash. Neem leaves can also be used in the bathwater of both adults and children to relieve itching.[13]

Infants and young children may have their skin washed with a mild Neem baby soap, as directed.

Psoriasis

After acne, psoriasis is the second most common skin disease, which affects between 0.1 – 3 percent of people worldwide. Widely known among most races, but more predominant in the West, it is one of the oldest medically documented skin disorders. It affects around 125 million people, although doctors have often misdiagnosed it as leprosy, dermatitis or eczema.

---

[12] Biswas, K., Chattopadhyay, I., Banerjee, R. K., & Bandyopadhyay, U. (2002). *Biological activities and medicinal properties of neem (Azadirachta indica)*.Current science, 82(11), 1336-1345.
[13] Hashmat, I., Azad, H., & Ahmed, A. (2012). *Neem (Azadirachta indica A. Juss)-A nature's drugstore: an overview*. Int Res J Biol Sci, 1, 76-79.

Psoriasis presents as a chronic relapsing auto immune disease characterized by itchy, dry, red and flaky papules and plaques distributed on the scalp, elbows, knees, hands, feet, and genitals. Generalized symptoms may include aching joints, pitted fingernails and toenails, burning and itching eyes, tiredness and listlessness.

The standard medical treatment for psoriasis has been either topical coal tar ointment or cortisone cream. These can have side effects, including skin thinning in the case of topical steroids, while coal tar is a smelly carcinogen that can cause skin to become sensitive to light.

Neem has none of these drawbacks since topical applications of Neem, as soap, cream, lotion, or shampoo are inexpensive and can be used for extended periods without any negative side effects for a variety of psoriasis types, including:

- **Plaque psoriasis**: is the most common type with red, inflamed skin lesions coated by silvery white scales (plaques) made up of dead skin cells. When these scaly lesions are scraped off they reveal tiny bleeding points in the skin below. This is known as the Auspitz sign and confirms the diagnosis of psoriasis.
- **Guttate psoriasis**: often starts in childhood and is characterized by small red dots or lesions that can be heavily distributed on the trunk, limbs, scalp, face and ears. It can come on suddenly or flare up after certain triggers.
- **Pustular psoriasis:** typically characterized by blisters filled with white blood cells. The condition causes reddening of the skin, pustule information, and scaling, but is not contagious.
- **Inverse psoriasis**: generally appears as smooth inflamed lesions without scaling and becomes easily irritated by rubbing and

sweating since it appears mostly in body folds, such as underarms and groin.

- **Erythrodermic psoriasis**: the most serious, acutely inflammatory form, characterized by red inflammatory lesions over large areas of the skin and systemic reactions such as wide spread swelling, pain, unstable body temperature, cardiac and infectious complications. This condition can result in death and requires urgent medical treatment and stabilization before other treatments are applied.

Psoriasis can be aggravated by: 1. Emotional and physical stress. 2. Physical irritations such as cuts, burns, rashes or insect bites. 3. Infectious triggers such as viral and bacterial infections. 4. Medications such as beta blockers or withdrawal from medications such as cortisone. 5. Vaccinations. 6. Sunburn, poor nutrition, alcohol or drugs and many other factors.

Psoriasis may flare for weeks or months, before subsiding for a period with no symptoms, only to return, sometimes with a vengeance. Many sufferers have found that Neem helps to break this cycle.

Suggestions: Wash the affected area with Neem soap and the scalp with Neem shampoo. Dry thoroughly and apply Neem cream, lotion or oil to skin. A couple of Neem leaves in the bath will help settle down inflammation and itching. Adults and teenagers can also take Neem capsules as directed.

For infants a Neem leaf can be added to the bathwater and a gentle Neem baby soap can be used as recommended by your health practitioner.

Studies show that Neem has cleared up psoriasis, often after many other treatments have failed. Millions of psoriasis sufferers have found relief from the Neem tree without any negative side effects. [14]

USING NEEM FOR OTHER COMMON SKIN CONDITIONS

Athlete's Foot

Known as tinea pedis, athlete's foot is a common fungal infection of the feet which is picked up in public pools, spas and saunas. It starts with small, water-filled blisters that soon become moist, inflamed, itchy patches that settle between the toes, around the toenails, and on calloused areas of the sole. Poor hygiene, wearing synthetic socks and footwear and sweaty feet produce favorable conditions for the growth of the fungus.

Wash feet with Neem soap. Dry thoroughly and apply Neem cream or lotion to affected areas.

Boils/Carbuncles

Both are painful, infected pustules that form under the skin when bacteria infect one or more of the hair follicles. Boils (furuncles) usually start as red, tender lumps and quickly fill with pus, grow larger and more painful until they rupture and drain. A carbuncle is a cluster of boils forming a connected raft of infection under the skin.

Topical Neem will help heal and disinfect these pustules.

---

[14] Cornborough, J. (1994) *Neem: An ancient cure for a modern world.* Positive Health: Complementary Health Magazine.

Canker Sore
Also called aphthous mouth ulcers; they are small sores that appear inside the cheeks, on the lips and the tongue. They are common but have no known cause. Use a Neem mouth gel made for this purpose.

Cellulitis
This is an acute bacterial infection of the skin and subcutaneous tissue which is sometimes triggered when the skin has been broken through cracks, cuts, blisters, burns, insect bites, or medical procedures. Legs are most commonly affected with areas that are red, hot and painful.

In conjunction with medical treatment, studies show that topical Neem preparations may be beneficial as a treatment for cellulitis, since it is a potent antibacterial.[15]

Corns/Calluses
Both corns and calluses are found on the feet as thickened areas of skin that can become painful. They are usually caused by excessive pressure or friction on the skin from poorly fitting shoes. Try rubbing the area with a bit of Neem oil for relief. [16]

Diaper Rash
Many parents still use petrochemical derived petroleum gel for diaper rash, which does not allow the skin to breathe. Neem cream or lotion specially formulated for this purpose helps to heal and soothe baby's skin.

---

[15] Sarmiento, W. C., Maramba, C. C. et al. (2011). *An in-vitro study on the antibacterial effect of neem (Azadirachta indica) leaf extract on methicillin-sensitive and Methicillin-resistant Staphylococcus aureus*. PIDSP J,12, 40-45.
[16] Hanau, A (1995). *Die Ringelblume:* Botanic, Chemie, Pharma.

Herpes/Cold Sores

Herpes is a contagious viral infection characterized by red and tingly skin areas prior to a breakout into small blisters in areas such as the mouth, throat and genitals. Triggers include emotional and physical stress, and a weakened immune system through infections or immune lowering medications.

Neem extract has been shown to be effective against the herpes simplex type 1 virus. [17] Adults can use Neem soap, cream, lotion or topical oral gel on the lesions, depending on their location.

Impetigo

Also called school sores, infants and children are usually affected by impetigo, a highly contagious skin infection caused by staphylococcus and streptococcus bacteria. The bacteria invade the skin through a small cut, scrape or a scratched bug bite, and can cause two types of impetigo. The non-bullous is more common, appearing as red sores on the face, especially around the nose and mouth, which burst and ooze before scabbing over with crusts. Bullous impetigo is less common and causes large blisters which spread to other parts of the body.

Neem has been found to demonstrate antibacterial activity against both staphylococcus and streptococcus bacteria causing impetigo.[18]

---

[17] Tiwari,V., Darmani, N. et al (2010). *In vitro antiviral activity of neem (Azardirachta indica L.) bark extract against herpes simplex virus type 1 infection.* Phytotherapy Research, 24(8), 1132-1140.
[18] Sarmiento, W. C., Maramba, C. C. et al. (2011). *An in-vitro study on the antibacterial effect of neem (Azadirachta indica) leaf extract on methicillin-sensitive and Methicillin-resistant Staphylococcus aureus.* PIDSP J,12, 40-45.

For babies, use a gentle Neem baby soap on affected skin, rinse and pat dry, or as directed by your health practitioner. Children may be bathed with gentle Neem soap, followed by a topical application of Neem cream or lotion, as directed.

Ringworm

Ringworm (tinea corporis) is a contagious fungal infection that affects the skin around the arms, legs or face in circular patches. It affects mainly children and is characterized by small red spots that grow into red, scaly ¼ inch patches with raised edges. Neem has been found to be effective against the fungus types (dermatophytes) that cause tinea.[19]

In children, wash area with gentle Neem soap, pat dry and apply a gentle Neem cream or lotion to affected area until infection subsides, or as directed by your health practitioner.

Rosacea

Rosacea is a chronic skin condition similar to facial acne, appearing in adults over thirty. In severe cases the nose may become red, swollen and bumpy from excess inflammation and pustule formation. Neem has been found to effectively reduce the inflammation of rosacea.[20]

Wash affected area with Neem soap, pat dry and apply Neem cream or lotion. In severe cases, adults may take oral Neem capsules or tinctures to boost the immune system.

---

[19] Natarajan, V., Venugopal, P. V., & Menon, T. (2003). *Effect of Azadirachta indica (neem) on the growth pattern of dermatophytes.* Indian Journal of Medical Microbiology, *21*(2), 98.
[20] Dhamane, S., Asnani, G., Kulkarni, A. S., Khandekar, V., & Hukkeri, V. I. (2012). *Development and evaluation of herbal anti-dandruff hair gel.* World J Pharmacy Pharm Sci, *1*(3), 1173-79.

Scabies

Scabies is an intensely itchy and infectious rash, characterized by small red bumps and blisters, caused by a mite, Sarcoptes scabiei, which burrows under the skin to lay its eggs. The rash occurs in characteristic places, including the sides and webs of the fingers, elbows, underarms, the belly button and waist, as well as knees, buttocks and thighs. Young children may get scabies on their scalp. The mite is generally spread through direct contact with an infected person or through clothing or bedding and it can survive away from a host for 24 to 36 hours in colder weather. Symptoms of scabies typically begin three to six weeks after the first exposure.

Studies show that Neem is effective against both scabies and head lice. [21] For adults, wash skin with Neem soap, pat dry and apply Neem oil to affected areas. Repeat for 3 -15 days until rash subsides.

For infants and young children, consult your health practitioner.

---

[21] Biswas, K., Chattopadhyay, I., Banerjee, R. K., & Bandyopadhyay, U. (2002). *Biological activities and medicinal properties of neem (Azadirachta indica).*Current science, 82(11), 1336-1345.

Neem and General Health

From the bitterness of disease man learns the sweetness of health.

Catalan proverb

 Research has shown that Neem has a wider use and efficacy than any other herb used to treat human illness. Ayurvedic practitioners have used Neem for millennia in the treatment of countless health problems as well as maintaining and enhancing good health.

All components of the Neem tree, including: bark, twigs, seeds, fruit, gum, leaves, flower, root, cake, wood and Neem seed oil contain at least one of the 135 active constituents that offer impressive healing qualities across a wide range of human health conditions. Their beneficial effects include:

* Anti-anxiety: capable of preventing anxiety.
* Anti-inflammatory: effective in alleviating inflammation.
* Anti-bacterial/viral/fungal: able to destroy or inhibit the growth of harmful microorganisms without damaging beneficial bacteria that maintain optimal health.
* Anti-carcinogenic: counteracts the effect of a carcinogen or inhibits the development of cancer.
* Anti-emetic: able to prevent nausea and vomiting.
* Anti-feedant: inhibits normal insect feeding behavior.
* Anti-fertility: capable of producing contraceptive effects.
* Anti-oxidant: may protect cells from the damage caused by unstable molecules known as free radicals (cancer causing).

- Anti-pyretic: able to lower the body temperature, prevent and or alleviate fever.
- Anti-helminthic: capable of eliminating parasitic intestinal worms.
- Anti-tumor: able to reduce tumor growth.
- Analgesic: able to relieve pain.
- Alterative: able to cure or restore health.
- Immune system booster and simulator: Neem stimulates infection-fighting T- cells.
- Nutrient: Neem oil is especially high in important fatty acids essential for maintaining lipid health.

Using Natural Remedies Wisely

Neem products have been successfully used to treat a variety of common ailments in adults in both ancient and modern times. The following information is intended for educational purposes only. Please seek the guidance of a natural medicine qualified health or medical professional for treatment of children, pregnant or breast feeding women or in case of serious illness. Neem should not be used by persons with allergies to Neem products.

Allergy

Seek medical advice in case of severe allergy. For dry skin, itchy eyes and runny nose associated with hay fever or stings, apply Neem cream, oil or leaf extract externally to the skin. A course of Neem tea, tincture or capsules may be taken internally, as directed. [22]

Asthma

---

[22] Conrick, J. (2001). *Neem: The ultimate herb.* Lotus Press.

Seek medical advice in case of acute asthma episode. As a complementary treatment, use Neem tea, oil, tincture or capsules, as directed, over a period of time. Neem oil applied to flooring and home surfaces can also eradicate dust mites that may trigger asthma. [23]

Birth Control (Women)

Vaginal creams and pessaries containing Neem oil have been found to be an effective vaginal contraceptive in women. When used just prior to intercourse, or even immediately afterwards, it has been shown to be a strong spermicide without unwanted side effects. This simple remedy promises to be a miraculous and safe solution to global overpopulation. [24]

Birth Control (Men)

Preliminary studies show that Neem extracts reduce fertility in male animals without lowering libido or sperm production. More research is needed for use in humans. [25]

Cancer

A glycoprotein found in the Neem leaf (NLGP) and other Neem compounds have been found to inhibit the growth of tumor cells in animals and humans in a variety of cancers. This may lead to future development of non toxic cancer treatments. [26]

Cardiovascular

---

[23] Biswas, K., Chattopadhyay, I. et al. (2002). *Biological activities and medicinal properties of neem (Azadirachta indica).*Current science, 82(11), 1336-1345.

[24] Sinha, K. Riar, S. et al. (1984). *Neem oil as a vaginal contraceptive.* Indian Journal of Medical Research, 79, 131-6.

[25] Lilot, L. S. (2000). *The Neem Tree: The Village Pharmacy.* Ethnobotanical Leaflets (1) 9.

[26] Chakraborty, K. et al. (2010). *Restoration of dysregulated CC chemokine signaling for monocyte/macrophage chemotaxis in head and neck squamous cell carcinoma patients by neem leaf glycoprotein maximizes tumor cell cytotoxicity.* Cellular & molecular immunology 7(5) 396-408.

Several beneficial effects of nimbidin and other compounds found in Neem leaves have been shown in animal studies to benefit the cardio vascular system by reducing high blood pressure, lowering cholesterol levels, preventing blood clots and slowing down rapid heartbeat. These promising results are being studied for therapeutic use in humans. [27] [28]

Chagas Disease

Also called the American sleeping sickness, it is caused by the blood sucking kissing bug (Triatomines) which feeds on humans at night and inoculates the host with a disease-causing parasite (Trypanosoma cruzi). The disease is characterized by fever, swollen lymph nodes and it eventually causes heart problems in 30% of sufferers.

It was once thought to be endemic to Mexico and South America but has been found to migrate further north into the US. Neem extracts are found to prevent the parasite from surviving in the human host, and when given to the kissing bug, Neem prevents the kissing bug from acquiring the disease and transmitting it to humans. [29]

Neem leaf or seed extracts can be sprayed around the home to prevent infestations and Neem tea can be drunk once daily to help prevent the disease. [30]

---

[27] Chattopadhyay, R. R. (1997). *Effect of Azadirachta indica hydroalcoholic leaf extract on the cardiovascular system.* General Pharmacology: The Vascular System, 28(3), 449-451.
[28] Koley, K. M., & Lal, J. (1994). *Pharmacological effects of Azadirachta indica (neem) leaf extract on the ECG and blood pressure of rat.* Indian journal of physiology and pharmacology, 38(3), 223-225.
[29] Beard, J. (1989). *Tree may hold the key to curbing chagas parasite.* New Scientist Pg, 124.
[30] Garcia, E. S., Gonzalez, M. S., & Rembold, H. (1989). *Chagas disease and its insect vector. Curing effect of azadirachtin A in the triatomine host, Rhodnius prolixus, from its parasite, Trypanosoma cruzi. In Host Regulated Developmental Mechanisms in Vector Arthropods (pp. 263-269).* University of Florida Vero Beach.

Chicken pox

Treat skin lesions with Neem leaf paste or cream to soothe inflammation and promote healing. Neem capsules or tea as directed for antiviral action to help eliminate the varicella (chicken pox) virus from the body. [31]

Chronic fatigue and fibromyalgia

When chronic fatigue is caused by post viral illness or chemical exposure Neem capsules, tincture or tea, when used as directed, may help with chronic pain, debility, fatigue and poor immune and adrenal function, typical of these conditions. [32]

Constipation

Use Neem capsules, tincture or tea, as directed, for relief of constipation. [33]

Dark circles around eyes

If no underlying illness has been diagnosed by your doctor, make a paste of water and Neem powder and apply it to skin around eyes, wash it off after 15 minutes. Do this for a few weeks to see an improvement.

Dengue fever

The extract of Neem leaves has been shown to inhibit the dengue virus type 2 which causes the severe viral hemorrhagic fever that is now responsible for 390 million cases in 100 countries around the world. [34]

---

[31] Singh, U. P., & Singh, D. P. (2002). *Neem in human and plant disease therapy.*Journal of herbal pharmacotherapy, 2(3), 13-28.

[32] Panossian, A. G. (2003). *Adaptogens: tonic herbs for fatigue and stress..*Alternative & Complementary Therapies, 9(6), 327-331.

[33] Biswas, K., Chattopadhyay, I., et al. (2002). *Biological activities and medicinal properties of neem (Azadirachta indica)*.Current science, 82(11), 1336-1345.

[34] Parida, M. M., Upadhyay, C. et al. (2002*). Inhibitory potential of neem (Azadirachta indica Juss) leaves on dengue virus type-2 replication.* Journal of Ethnopharmacology, 79(2), 273-278.

Dental and oral care

It is estimated that over 90% of North Americans suffer from some type of dental disease. Gum infections, including bleeding and sore gums and tooth decay, have been treated very successfully through the application of Neem mouthwash, Neem toothpaste or leaf extract. Some users have reported a total reversal of gum inflammation and bleeding after using Neem for only a few weeks or months.

Traditionally, throughout the centuries, India's village people have used Neem tree twigs to brush their teeth, which has maintained the incidence of tooth decay and gum disease at remarkably low levels, considering that village populations have often had limited access to modern dental care. [35]

Diabetes

Neem has been shown to reduce the need for insulin among diabetics and may be a valuable adjunct to treatment. Consult your health practitioner for advice.[36]

Digestive disorders

Neem tincture or capsules have been shown to be effective remedies for the relief of heartburn, indigestion, peptic or duodenal ulcer pain, gastritis and hemorrhoids. [37] [38]

Diarrhea and Dysentery

Use Neem leaves, tea, capsules or tincture as directed. [39]

---

[35] www.7stepsdentalhealth.com

[36] Bailey, C. J., & Day, C. (1989). *Traditional plant medicines as treatments for diabetes.* Diabetes care, 12(8), 553-564.

[37] Lans, C. (2007) *Ethnobiology and Ethnomedicine.* Journal of Ethnobiology and Ethnomedicine, 3, 3.

[38] Garg, G. P., Nigam, S. K., & Ogle, C. W. (1993). *The gastric antiulcer effects of the leaves of the neem tree.* Planta medica, 59(3), 215-217.

Fungi, parasites, viruses

Although its exact mechanism of action remains unknown, Neem has been shown to destroy harmful fungi, parasites, bacteria and viruses without destroying beneficial gut and skin bacteria.

Neem capsules, oil or tincture have been used to treat athlete's foot, thrush, intestinal and skin parasite infestations and herpes viruses by destroying the micro-organisms or parasites responsible, and reducing inflammation.

A number of clinical studies have shown Neem to be effective against several bacterial strains including: Stapylococus aureus, Streptococcus pyogenes, and Corynebacterium, E.coli, and Salmonella typhosa. These bacteria are responsible for causing meningitis, cystitis, sore throats, typhoid, blood poisoning and food poisoning. [40]

Neem's effectiveness against parasites is due to compounds that interrupt the life cycle of parasites by inhibiting the ability of the parasites to feed and reproduce, and by preventing parasite eggs from hatching. Neem has been effective against lice and the mites that cause scabies. [41]

Intestinal worm infestations are treated and prevented throughout the tropics by traditional use of Neem teas. [42]

---

[39] Gupta, R., Vairale, M. et al. (2009). *Ethnomedicinal Plants Used by Gond Tribe of Bhandara District, Maharashtra in the Treatment of Diarrhoea and Dysentery.* Ethnobotanical Leaflets, 2009(7), 7.

[40] De, N., & Ifeoma, E. (2002). *Antibacterial effects of components of the bark extract of neem (Azadirachta indica A. Juss).* Technol. Dev, 8, 23-28.

[41] Heukelbach, J., Oliveira, F. A., & Speare, R. (2006). *A new shampoo based on neem (Azadirachta indica) is highly effective against head lice in vitro.* Parasitology research, 99(4), 353-356.

[42] Biswas, K., Chattopadhyay, I. et al. (2002). *Biological activities and medicinal properties of neem (Azadirachta indica).* Current Science, 82. 1336-1345.

Traditionally, Ayurveda has used Neem seed oil, pastes, tinctures, extracts and powder for the prevention and treatment of infectious and parasitic diseases in India. Increasingly, Neem is used in the West to treat these conditions.

Hair, scalp and nails

When quality organic wild crafted Neem leaf extracts are added to personal care and beauty preparations, they provide many extra health and beauty benefits without side effects. Problem scalp conditions such as dandruff, psoriasis, scaling and even hair loss respond to treatments with Neem shampoo, soap, cream, capsules and tinctures.

Dry, damaged and overly oily hair also responds to this amazing plant.

Brittle nails will benefit from a few drops of Neem oil. Even nails that have turned yellow due to chronic fungal infections often return to their normal condition after treatment with Neem.

Hepatitis

Neem leaf extract has been shown to inhibit the hepatitis B virus and may assist in the treatment of the disease when used as directed and with practitioner supervision. [43]

HIV/AIDS

Neem leaf extract has been studied in HIV/AIDS patients and found to decrease the viral load and increase the function of the immune system while being safe and without side effects. [44]

---

[43] Joseph, B., & Raj, S. J. (2011). *A comparative study on various properties of five medicinally important plants*. International Journal of Pharmacology, 7(2), 206-211.

Leucoderma (Vitiligo)

An acquired and non-infectious skin condition characterized by patchy loss of pigmentation that may occur after trauma to the skin from burns, injections or dermabrasion, or after inflammatory conditions. May improve with Neem oil or cream used on skin as directed. [45]

Liver function

Neem helps protect the liver from damage from chemicals, drugs and pollutants. Neem leaf has been shown to minimize chemically induced liver damage by stabilizing levels of serum marker enzymes and boosting levels of antioxidants which neutralize free radicals and prevent cellular damage. [46]

Malaria

Active ingredients in Neem leaves, including azadirachtin and irodin A are toxic to resistant strains of malaria. In vitro studies have shown 100% mortality of malaria organisms in seventy-two hours with a 1:20000 dilution ratio.

Neem tea, capsules or tincture may be useful in the treatment and prevention of malaria, when used as directed. [47] [48]

---

[44] Mbah, A. U., Udeinya, I. et al. (2007). *Fractionated neem leaf extract is safe and increases CD4+ cell levels in HIV/AIDS patients.* American journal of therapeutics, 14(4), 369-374.

[45] Awasthi, N., Khan, K., Sahu, A., & Singh, A. K. (2012). *Neem (Azadirachta indica)-A Devine Medicine. Advances in Life Sciences,* 1(1), 10-12.

[46] Chattopadhyay, R. (2003). *Possible mechanism of hepatoprotective activity of Azadirachta indica leaf extract:* Part II. Journal of Ethnopharmacology, 89(2), 217-219.

[47] Jones, I. W., Denholm, A. et al. (1994). *Sexual development of malaria parasites is inhibited in vitro by the neem extract azadirachtin, and its semi-synthetic analogues.* FEMS microbiology letters, 120(3), 267-273.

[48] Abatan, M. O., & Makinde, M. J. (1986). *Screening Azadirachta indica and Pisum sativum for possible antimalarial activities.* Journal of ethnopharmacology, 17(1), 85-93.

Minor skin injuries

Minor abrasions, burns, sprains and bruises are easily treated with Neem cream, lotion or Neem leaf extract and applied locally as directed. The anti-inflammatory and antibacterial attributes of Neem are healing and soothing.

Neuroprotective

Animal studies have confirmed that antioxidant compounds in Neem help to prevent brain damage after stroke and in case of lead poisoning. More studies are underway in humans. [49]

Personal and household insecticide

Neem oil effectively repels a wide variety of common garden bugs including caterpillars, mematodes, locust, aphids, Japanese beetles and mites.

In agriculture, Neem extracts have been approved by the US Environmental Protection Agency for use on food crops. These are non-toxic to humans, birds, animals and beneficial insects.

In the home, Neem oil can be used to combat ants, cockroaches, flies, termites, mosquitoes and bed bug infestations.

Neem oil can be used topically, as directed, on skin as a personal insect repellent. [50]

---

[49] Yanpallewar, S., Rai, S. et al. (2005). *Neuroprotective effect of Azadirachta indica on cerebral post-ischemic reperfusion and hypoperfusion in rats.* Life sciences, 76(12), 1325-1338.
[50] Maramoroch, K. (1997*). The neem tree: source of unique natural products for integrated pest management, medicine, industry and other purposes..* Environmental Entomology, 26(3), 726-726.

Neem Honey

The honey is produced from the nectar of the Neem flower, is slightly bitter and has a light amber colour with a low viscosity. Highly valued in ancient Ayurvedic medicine for its medicinal properties, Neem honey is known to be beneficial in lowering high blood pressure and acts as a blood purifier.

When one to two teaspoons are taken twice daily, it is a nutritious food which can also assist in the treatment of allergies, dental diseases, throat infections or skin problems.

Finding a Natural Medicine Practitioner

Mainstream medicine would be very effective if it gave a fraction of its time and effort to prevention rather than intervention.

Unknown

Most people are frustrated when they ask their doctor about natural medicine and many are met with blank looks or worse, stern disapproval for merely mentioning the topic.

This stems from the fact that no medical student in the Western world is currently taught the academic research and skills that underpin the use of nutritionals and botanicals. This accounts for medical doctors having virtually no working knowledge of natural medicines.

Many doctors become irritated at the mere mention of the subject and, as a knee jerk response, advise their patients to abandon any form of natural medicine, sometimes claiming that it may be harmful (a dubious claim since few, if any, deaths have been directly attributable to the therapeutic use of natural medicines compared to the millions of deaths around the world caused by pharmaceuticals). [51]

---

[51] Despite the impressive safety record of natural remedies, it is still advisable to consult a practitioner with expertise in natural medicine for advice.

In short, we cannot expect the average doctor to be able to treat us with natural medicines unless he/she has had special training. We can however, find an expert herbalist or naturopath with this skill and they are usually happy to work alongside any medical protocols prescribed by your doctor . Natural medicine treatments are versatile and can be used in conjunction with conventional medicine treatment, or for simple conditions, as a sole treatment.

Getting reliable advice is even more important since most people rely on the internet for information and become confused by the sheer numbers of natural medicines and protocols presented by almost anyone, whether they are qualified or not. Despite this, millions of people have no doubt found relief from the simple remedies found there, and from online Neem products.

But for more complex or serious conditions, it is advisable to consult your medical doctor as well as a qualified herbalist, or naturopath. This way you can benefit from both conventional medical interventions as well as the healing that natural medicine promotes. You can then be certain that these professionals are trained in the correct and effective use of natural and herbal medicines while avoiding possible herb and medication interactions. Perhaps you can locate an integrative medicine physician or holistic medical doctor in your area, who is trained in both conventional and natural medicine, but these are not found in great numbers.

I can almost hear you say: 'Easier said than done!' Those who set out to look for a natural medicine practitioner might soon become confused by the many different names for such professionals, as well as the misinformation out there on the topic of natural medicine. This has its origins in the fundamental differences between natural and conventional medicine and the current politics of medicine.

First of all, the clinical practice of natural medicine is philosophically different from conventional medicine. Emergency medicine is the exclusive domain of conventional medical practice, in which natural medicine plays virtually no role. However, in the treatment of chronic illness, natural medicines can often assist the body to heal from imbalance and illness, while conventional medicine offers mainly synthetic drugs or interventions for the temporary relief of symptoms.

On this note, here's what Debra St. Claire, master herbalist, has to say:

*After the ability to synthesize medicine from inert substances such as petroleum and minerals was developed, the therapeutic use of herbs diminished. The art of pharmacy turned to the production of drugs which could bring the quickest relief of **symptoms,** ignoring the reason that the symptoms appeared. As we look back, perhaps it is time to reconsider the path. The use of these substances has spawned a myriad of unexpected problems, such as suppression of the very signals that our bodies produce to alert us to a need of change. Pain itself is a call to action — a call to remedy the imbalance in our lifestyle. The proficient use of herbal therapy is directly connected to our ability to sense that first signal and to adjust our lifestyle accordingly. It is when these signals are continually ignored that disease has a chance to seat itself more deeply within our bodies. The appropriate use of herbs is only one of many health alternatives to our present medical system.* [52]

This different outlook on treating human illness probably accounts for the reason that so few medical doctors are able to embrace both sides of healing. One is about sickness and the other about wellness. Once the medical emergency is over, the body can use all the natural help it can get to heal itself.

---

[52] St. Claire D. (1993) *Pocket Herbal Reference Guide.* Crossing Press.

For more on the healing approach of natural medicine and using herbs, master herbalist Debra St. Claire says this:

A medical herbalist tries to diagnose the cause of the health problem, provides accurate information on any possible contraindications and/or drug-herb interactions. After the patient is thoroughly consulted, a personalized health program is created by treating the whole person and customized herbal formulations are blended together for a unique health picture. Medical herbalists are highly trained practitioners that combine the use of botanical medicine, science, nutrition and supplements to restore health and are trained in the same diagnostic skills as orthodox doctors but take a more holistic approach to illness. They have completed 4 years of studying herbal medicine; have had extensive training in anatomy, physiology, pathology, clinical assessment, pharmacology, biochemistry, botany, materia medica, philosophy of herbal medicine and therapeutics and nutrition. [53]

Another source of public confusion lies in the vast array of terminology which has muddled the meaning of natural medicine in the mind of the average medical consumer. Here's what Dr. Carolyn Dean MD, ND, physician, herbalist, nutritionist and acupuncturist writes on that issue: [54]

It is against our belief to use terms such as alternative, complementary or CAM (Complementary and Alternative), except when quoting. It is unfortunate that the medical establishment and all too many of my colleagues who practice [conventional allopathic] medicine have fallen into the habit of calling the oldest and most successful form of healing by what are, in fact, demeaning names, such as complementary and alternative. We must always remember that allopathy is only a medical model born in the

---

[53] St. Claire D. (1992) Pocket Herbal Reference Guide.
[54] Dean C. (2008) *Death by Modern Medicine - seeking safe solutions.* Independent Publisher. (Quoted with permission)

industrial age, and to suggest that the oldest and most used healing arts in the world are secondary to allopathy is not only insulting but inaccurate as well. These traditional methods of restoring and maintaining maximum health, by virtue of their track record of safety and success, take second place to no other medial model.

Since the CAM terminology is in common use, at least until a more suitable name can be found, I will provide a short list of practitioners qualified to practice natural medicine, for people who want professional guidance with natural remedies. These include:

- Integrative physicians (use both conventional and natural medicine).
- Holistic physicians (as above).
- Qualified naturopaths (with tertiary degrees are trained in use of natural medicines and other modalities).
- Naturopathic doctors (as above).
- Osteopathic physicians (use a variety of natural medicine modalities).
- Qualified herbalists (are trained in use of herbal medicines).
- Qualified practitioners of traditional Chinese medicine (as above).
- Qualifed Ayurvedic physician (use a variety of natural medicine modalities).

Each has a holistic approach to health care and should be duly qualified and registered in their state to administer natural medicine to patients, either as a treatment for simple conditions, or as an adjunct to standard medical treatments, in case of a more serious or complex illness.

Part 3

Science of Neem

Science is organized knowledge. Wisdom is organized life.

Immanuel Kant

The Neem tree is an attractive broad-leaf evergreen which is a member of the mahogany family. It is an ancient plant that has come down through the eons to become one of the most versatile and widely used plants on earth today.

The Neem tree's Sanskrit name is 'Arishtha' meaning reliever of sickness, and its most useful application has traditionally been considered 'sarbaroganibarini', a reliever of skin ailments.

Neem has been traditionally used in Ayurvedic medicine, Unani medicine of South Asia and as extracts in Western herbal medicine.

Only in recent decades have intense scientific investigations of the properties of Neem been conducted. Over the past 20 years, scientists have published more than 2000 research papers about Neem's environmental and medicinal uses.

The first attempt to extract compounds from the Neem tree occurred in 1942, when Professor Salimuzzaman Siddiqui, working at Hussain Ebrahim Jamal Research Institute of Chemistry, Karachi, discovered some novel and useful compounds from the Neem tree. Using a chemical extraction process, he had isolated three compounds from Neem oil, which he named, nimbin, nimbinin, and nimbidin. Of the three, he identified nimbidin as the main active component in the Neem oil. However, all three compounds were found to be chemically stable natural insecticides which also had considerable medicinal activity, including anthelmintic, antifungal, antibacterial, and antiviral properties.

For his work, Professor Siddiqui was awarded the Order of the British Empire in 1946. He continued to discover and isolate numerous unique antibacterial compounds from various parts (leaves, bark etc.) of the Neem tree and other plants until he had patented over 50 chemical compounds in his name. Most of these discoveries still remain vital natural ingredients of various medicines as well as bio-pesticides.

Based on this and other scientific work, several important organizations have recognized the importance of Neem, including; the U.S. Department of Agriculture, National Research Council, U.S. Agency for International Development, National Academy of Sciences and the Institute of Medicine.

In 1992, the Board of Science and the Technology for International Development published a definitive book entitled 'Neem – a tree for solving global problems'. The book was based on two decades of research and listed Neem's wide range of benefits for health and healing.

According to the National Research Council (NRC), Neem alone seems to offer the greatest potential for solving global agricultural and environmental problems with its myriad of exploitable by-products. Some scientists believe that this plant may usher in a new era in non-toxic pest control while also being capable of reducing erosion, deforestation and excessive climate change. Agro scientists confirm that Neem is the most eco-friendly pesticide currently known to science and farmers don't need a science degree to use it. The Neem kernels can be mixed with compost to rot. This causes the pesticidal compounds such as azadirachtin, salanin and nimbin to leach out, making the insect killing compost ready to be used in three to four months, depending on the weather. These Neem compounds contain potent anti-feedant properties that are repugnant to over 500 species of crop destroying insects.

Natural Neem compounds are far safer than the currently used organophosphate class of chemical pesticides that are harmful to humans, animals and to useful insects such as bees. Over the years, many experts have expressed skepticism about a plant that seems able to perform such a wide variety of functions, but no more. In his article, *An Introduction to Neem*, author Dr Dan Sindelar notes; 'The National Academy of Sciences stated "Even some of the most cautious researchers are now saying that Neem deserves to be called a wonder plant"'.

A class of healing compounds in Neem
Scientists have so far identified and isolated more than 135 chemical compounds from different parts of the Neem plant. They include a class of organic chemicals called isoprenoids. These fascinating naturally occurring chemicals include terpenes, diterpenoids and triterpenoid compounds. They have various biological activities that make them useful as traditional herbal remedies, including as antiseptic, antineoplastic, anti-inflammatory and insecticidal agents.

The major Neem compounds and their uses
- Nimbin - anti-inflammatory, anti-pyretic, antihistamine, anti-fungal
- Nimbidin - antibacterial, anti-ulcer, analgesic, anti-arrhythmic, anti-fungal
- Nimbidol - anti tubercular, anti-protozoan, anti-pyretic
- Gedunin - vasodilator, anti-malaria, anti-fungal

- Quercetin - anti-protozoa
- Saanen - repellent
- Azadirachtin - repellent, anti-feedant, anti-hormonal

Nutritional composition of fresh Neem Leaves

Moisture	59.4%
Proteins	7.1%
Fat	1.0%
Fibre	6.2%
Carbohydrates	22.9%
Minerals	3.4%
Calcium	510mg/100g
Phosphorous	80mg/100g
Iron	17mg/100g
Thiamine	0.04mg/100g
Niacin	1.40mg/100g
Vitamin C	218mg/100g
Carotene	1998 microgram/100g
Caloric value	1290 Kcal/kg
Glutamic acid	73.39mg/100g
Tyrosine	31.50mg/100g
Aspartic acid	15.50mg/100g
Alanine	6.40mg/100g
Proline	4.00mg/100g
Glutamine	1.00mg/100g

Courtesy of Dr. Vaidya Suresh Chaturvedi

The highest levels of nutrients and biologically active ingredients are found in the Neem seeds and oil, with the lesser amounts found in the bark and leaves.

Traditional Medicines

Ayurvedic medicines are produced in over 8400 pharmacies in India. Most of them are small neighbourhood pharmacies that compound Neem ingredients to make their own remedies.

Traditionally, Ayurvedic medicine recommends that the twigs and fresh leaves Neem leaves are used daily for mouth hygiene, tooth brushing and gum care.

More serious conditions such as malaria, arthritis, rheumatism or infections are treated with a concentrated paste of the Neem leaves or strong decoction of leaves and/or bark.

For skin, hair and scalp parasites, Neem oil is applied directly to the skin to release its insecticidal properties by direct contact. See part 2 for specific remedies to a variety of conditions.

Antioxidant compounds in Neem

Antioxidants are compounds that protect cells against chemicals or damaging rays that damage the body's DNA (free radical damage). This premature cell death can lead to many health conditions, including cancer, atherosclerosis, dementia, diabetes and premature aging.

Universities around the world have been testing the antioxidant compounds contained in a variety of plant foods including Neem. Findings indicate that Neem is high on the ORAC scale. This stands for oxygen radical absorbance capacity and is an indicator of a food's ability to counteract free radicals which prevents cellular damage and the onset of disease.

Food/Nutrient	ORAC capacity/gram
Blueberries	62.20
Broccoli	15.90
Cranberry	94.56
Grapefruit	15.48
Neem Bark	**476.00**
Neem Leaf	**357.00**
Neem Oil	**430.00**
Neem Supercritical Extract 8%	**114.00**
Plums	62.39
Spinach	26.40
Tomatoes	4.60

This chart shows that Neem components have some of the highest ORAC values available in vegetable matter.

Neem, Oil

Neem Oil

Neem oil is a vegetable oil obtained through pressing (crushing) of the seed kernels either through cold pressing or through a process incorporating temperature controls.

A large industry in India and China extracts the oil remaining in the seed cake using a solvent, hexane. This solvent-extracted oil is of a lower quality compared to the cold pressed oil and is mostly used for soap manufacturing. Neem cake is a by-product obtained from the solvent extraction process for Neem oil. It is perhaps the most important of the commercially available products of Neem.

The oil is generally light to dark brown, bitter with a rather strong odour that is said to combine the odours of peanut and garlic. It comprises mainly triglycerides and large amounts of triterpenoid compounds, which are responsible for its bitter taste. It is hydrophobic in nature and in order to emulsify it in water for application purposes, it must be formulated with appropriate surfactants.

Neem oil also contains steroids (campesterol, beta-sitosterol, stigmasterol), and a plethora of triterpenoids of which Azadirachtin is the most well known and studied. The Azadirachtin content of Neem oil varies from 300ppm to over 2000ppm depending on the quality of the Neem seeds/kernels crushed.

Neem oil has almost unlimited applications in agriculture, cosmetics and personal care, dental and medical uses, including treatments for head lice, massage oils and products for pets. Household and garden uses include the use of Neem oil as non-toxic pesticide, insect repellents and bio-pesticides for organic farms that are beneficial to honeybees and lady bugs and non-toxic to mammals, plants and birds. Its use includes controls for black spot, powdery mildew and anti-feedant spray for orchids etc.

Neem Genome
According to an Indian Press article published September 30, 2011, Indian scientists were the first to sequence the entire genome of Neem tree (Azadirachta indica), which includes all the organism's genetic materials. The breakthrough was achieved by a team of ten researchers at Ganit Labs of Bangalore, India.

I was privileged to meet the head of this lab, Professor Binday Panda, at the Neem Conference when he spoke about sequencing the Neem genome.

Professor Panda told the press conference: 'This is the first time the genome of a higher organism has been sequenced in India. We have traditionally known the medical properties of Neem'. The Professor added, 'Understanding its genetic complexity will help in developing agriculturally important compounds and pharmaceuticals. For instance, pesticidal compound Azadirachtin is found in Neem seeds in wildly varying concentrations. With genetic understanding and engineering, Azadirachtin content in Neem could potentially be increased and normalized'.

Ganit is a not-for-profit lab which collaborates with other scientists. Its findings will be submitted to a peer-reviewed journal for review and publication. It will also be setting up an online data bank where scientists around the world can access the genome architecture of the Neem tree.

Of all the plants that have provided traditional medicine with healing compounds, few have been scientifically proven to be as effective as Neem. This miraculous healing herb is both ancient and yet effective for a modern world.

I am pleased to have met Professor Panda, one of the scientists who has contributed to the research. Science has upheld the wisdom of the ages when it comes to this powerful natural medicine.

Politics of Neem

Our lives begin to end the day we become silent about the things that matter.

Dr Martin Luther King Jr.

Multinational corporations have taken a greater interest in traditional technologies and indigenous products after market research indicates that consumers are steering away from harmful, polluting and hazardous chemicals.

The relentless corporate search for technology, profits, and dominance in the marketplace has companies looking eastward toward natural products like Neem to cater to the global trend towards the use of consumer preferred safe and non-toxic products.

Many leading Western companies are now in the race to secure exclusive patents to Neem products. The American multinational chemical giant, W.R. Grace, has already successfully applied for a number of patents on Neem products, which in some cases includes the processes for extracting pesticides from the Neem tree seeds. In future, whoever wants to use such patented processes or products will have to pay a license fee to that corporation. These patents are enforced by the GATT agreement on international trade and apply equally to member states from the third world, including India, from which the Neem tree originated.

This application began a spate of patent applications, with USA based companies being granted the largest number of them (54), followed by Japan (35), Australia (23) and India (14). However, since 1995 India has more than 53 patent applications pending, which, if granted, will give its industry the highest number of patents with which to commercially use Neem products. In part, this is an attempt to prevent bio-piracy of the native Neem product by corporations in the Northern hemisphere.

Despite the many applications, of the 50 companies that tried to get patents on Neem products, about 70 patents were rejected. This has discouraged a few multinationals from pursuing research and development into Neem oil for agricultural application.

The flow of patents has occasionally encountered stiff resistance from activists. One such activist was Chandrashekhar Mahadeo Ketkar, better known as the 'Neem Man' who dedicated his life to spreading awareness of the properties and applications of Neem across the globe. He was also a staunch defender of Neem against those who applied to patent the plant.

In 2000, Ketkar joined forces with the Indian government and Indian NGO's led by environmentalist Dr. Vandana Shiva to challenge the European Patent Office on their new fungicide patent granted to the US firm WR Grace and the US Agriculture Department.

Ketkar and his fellow activists successfully challenged the patent on the grounds that Neem, as a natural product, could not be patented. The patent was revoked in 2005.

This success inspired the fight for revoking similar patents for turmeric and basmati rice.

Entomologist Ketkar had compiled a comprehensive *Neem Bibliography* in 1980 with over 1000 references, which sold more than 200 000 copies around the world. It was so popular among Neem enthusiasts that the occasional copy went 'missing', as was the case during the first World Neem Conference in Germany, in 1980.

Ketkar single-handedly founded and ran the acclaimed Neem Mission in Pune, India. Since 1990 his foundation has given out awards in recognition of achievements for pioneering work in entomology and agriculture related to Neem.

Numerous documentary and filmmakers have interviewed Ketkar about his Neem research, including: The CBC (Canadian Broadcasting Corporation), the German GIZ (Deutsche Gesellschaft fuer internationale Zusammenarbeit), the BBC, and the Tamil Nadu Agricultural University, among others.

During his lifetime, Ketkar traveled all over the world and was a self-confessed workaholic. 'If I had not remained a bachelor, I would not have been able to make my contribution', he told close relatives a few days before he died. He had suffered a heart attack in 2004 with 30% of his heart remaining non-functional, yet he lived another four years until 2007. He was 'surrounded by papers and worked until the end', said his brother's daughter-in-law Rohini Ketkar.

Among the most prominent of activists is Vandana Shiva PhD, originally trained as a physicist and philosopher. Instead she has become an environmentalist, author, eco-feminist and founder/director of the Research Foundation for Science, Technology, and Ecology in New Delhi. She has often opposed multinationals holding patents on life forms and argued that seeds are the cultural heritage of regional peoples, claiming that patents would impose royalty payments and prevent the use of a valuable commodity, resulting in impoverishment.

Dr Shiva has successfully assisted grassroots organizations of the emerging green movement in Africa, Latin America, Ireland, Switzerland, and Austria by helping local activists initiate campaigns against genetic engineering.

Vandana Shiva PhD

In the area of Intellectual Property rights (IPRs) and biodiversity, Dr. Shiva and her team at the Research Foundation for Science, Technology and Ecology successfully prevented the biopiracy of Neem, Basmati rice and wheat. She also played a role in the famous Chipko movement to save the Himalayan forest.

As mentioned before, a major test case occurred in September 1994 when the European Patent Office granted the United States Department of Agriculture and multinational company W.R. Grace a patent on the process to extract and stabilize an Aza A based pesticide derived from Neem seeds to be sold as an anti-fungal product US patent #5124349.

This action stirred up a wide cross section of stakeholders who disagreed that multinationals had the right to expropriate and exploit the fruits of centuries of indigenous experimentation and several decades of scientific research, for huge profits.

As a result Jeremy Rifkin, President of the Foundation on Economic Trends and Dr. Vandana Shiva, spearheaded a coalition, along with the International Federation of Organic Agriculture Movement, the Green Party in the European Parliament and 200 NGO's, Indian scientists, farmers and political activists from 45 countries. The group vehemently opposed granting of patents on Neem products to Western companies, claiming that the process for which the patent was granted had been in use in India for over 2000 years. Apart from this, they claimed that there cannot be a patent on Azadirachtin (Neem) because it is a product of nature and that patenting Neem based products and extracts constitutes an act of biological piracy.

In September 1995, Jeremy Rifkin and Dr Shiva petitioned the Patent Office to revoke Grace's patent. Although their petition was made primarily on legal grounds, their underlying objections reflected the following ethical and economic issues:

- 'Biological resources are part of the cultural heritage and should not be patented'.
- 'The patent will restrict the availability of living material to local people whose ancestors have spent centuries developing the material'.
- 'The patent may block economic growth in developing countries'.

Following a lengthy process lasting several years, the European Patent Office revoked the patent in 2000, but the victory was short lived after W.C. Grace mounted an appeal claiming that studies about the product and its application had never been published in a scientific journal prior to the patent application.

Five years later, after more than 100 000 Indian protesters and 225 agricultural, scientific and trade groups in 45 countries signed a petition protesting the move, the Patent Office once again revoked the patent at a hearing on March 9, 2005.

 Following this hard won victory, Dr Shiva said: 'We gave them evidence of farmers using this knowledge for a long time and also gave them information about the two scientists who had conducted research on Neem in the 1960s and 1970s before the patent had been granted. During the hearing, they dismissed the appeal and upheld the earlier revocation of the patent'. Calling it a historic moment, Dr. Shiva added: 'Patenting is one of the ways through which traditional users can be threatened. But now, such patents will no longer be a threat'.

As mentioned earlier, other aspects of Neem use continue to be patented; since 1975, the US Patent Office has published over 60 patents that refer to Neem.

The international challenge to W.R. Grace's patent marks the opening salvo of an ongoing battle between native peoples and traditional cultures versus transnational corporations for control over the genetic resources and bio diversity of the planet.

This battle for intellectual property rights to the global gene pool is likely to remain a critical political and economic issue for decades to come.

Since this global discussion centers on the Neem tree, it's no wonder that it has been called the 'billion dollar tree'. It is probably the most valuable biological real estate on earth and the knowledge on how to use it makes its commercial worth more than any other plant undergoing biological research.

The challenge mounted against the US Patent Office and W.R. Grace also has to be seen as a critical test of intellectual property laws under the new guidelines established by the World Trade Organization (WTO).

Indian farmers and health practitioners have been using Neem products for various purposes over centuries and these natural products are now highly sought after in the West.

In the field of agriculture, growing opposition to harmful synthetic pesticides and changing governmental regulatory policy in the West has also led to an intense interest in the pesticide properties of Neem.

For several decades, chemical insecticides were primarily synthetic, possessing a quick and toxic knockdown capability that endangered mammals and non-target organism. The toxicity was not of primary importance to regulators until recently when public pressure caused governments to require more safety regulations in the workplace and increased data requirements by regulators. This has greatly increased the demand for environmentally safe insecticides.

At the same time, older insecticides have lost patent protection, leading to cancelation of numerous expired registrations and reduced options available for insect control. This has opened the door to natural pesticides such as the Neem derived Azadirachtin, which is a metabolite found in Neem seeds. This compound has been classified as a biological insecticide for registration purposes by the U.S. Environmental Protection Agency (EPA), for which the data requirements have been less stringent due to the biological origin and safety profile of Neem.

The global trend towards the use of safe, alternative and ecologically beneficial agents has many leading Western companies continuing the race to secure the rights to Neem products and several have managed to secure patent rights for methods of extracting various natural chemicals from Neem in the form of an emulsion or solution.

As mentioned, activists like Dr Shiva claim that these modernized extraction processes can hardly be said to constitute a genuine innovation. They argue that these methods are simply an extension of the traditional processes used in India for centuries for making Neem based products, and that this technology was developed in India over centuries and has been made freely available to the world. By patenting them as their intellectual property, activists claim that Western companies are trying to monopolize these products and processes for their sole profit.

Western companies deny this and claim that the modernized processes are novel and an advance on traditional Indian techniques.

However, the moral force of the argument that Dr Shiva and other activists are using against biopiracy is attracting support from several unlikely quarters. The German member of the European Parliament for the Green Party, Hiltrud Breyer, who has been active in protesting against Neem patents in the European Patent Office (EPO), believes that Indians have cultivated and extended their knowledge of the Neem tree's versatile qualities for centuries. She agrees with Indian farmers that a multinational firm has no right to expropriate the agricultural achievements or resources of indigenous peoples, especially since that would impose a license fee on farmers who have traditionally taken their resources free from nature.

The activist community and much of the educated public generally agrees that indigenous people need to have their traditional rights to the Neem tree protected to ensure their continued use of the Neem tree as they have been doing over the past centuries. Public agencies, NGOs, farmer organizations and advocacy groups have played an important role in maintaining their rights.

However, the best option that will serve everyone seems to be twofold:

1. Encouraging the extensive use of existing Neem-based products as substitutes for risky, toxic chemical products.
2. Government funding of large scale research and development for the production of safe and eco-friendly Neem products for use in agriculture, industry, health care, environmental conservation and even family planning.

If this research is done methodically, and the Neem resource remains freely available, the vast benefits to farmers, companies and consumers will be life saving to humans, animals and the environment.

History and Future of Neem

The more things change, the more they are the same.

Alphonse Karr

Neem has been known from ancient times as a beneficial tree to humanity with a long history of use in Ayurvedic medicine. The tree is known in many cultures by many names, but its botanical name is Azadirachta indica. Some of its varied English names include: Indian Lilac, Margosa tree, nim, crackjack, paradise tree, white cedar and chinaberry.

Over the centuries, the Neem tree has gone from serving as the village pharmacy of small Indian towns to being the world's panacea.

Since the 1960s, the marketing of Neem began in earnest after the late C.M. Ketkar of Khadi & Village Industries Board of India commissioned a study on the potential of using Neem products in India. (This was reported in the documentary entitled *What's in a Neem* by presenter Dr. David Suzuki..)

Neem's popularity was further boosted by the pioneering work done by Professor Dr Heinrich Schmutterer and his colleagues investigating the chemistry and uses of Neem products and comprehensively documented in his book: *The Neem Tree.*

Since the 1960s, Indian industry saw an opportunity opening and soon a flourishing business began to grow; manufacturing Neem oil as bio-pesticides, Neem cake as organic manure, while Neem bark and leaf extracts were used to make a variety of creams, soap, shampoo, conditioners, tinctures, toothpaste, to name just a few.

Since then, interest in Neem products has spread, and they are now available in many different countries such as North America, Asia, Africa, Australia and Europe.

Futurists predict that the developing world, including Asia and Africa, will face many distressing crises in the next few decades caused by overpopulation, unsustainable use of natural resources, poverty, unemployment, and pollution.

Neem appears the answer to all of these issues, and to meet these challenges, many government and private greening initiatives have resulted in millions of Neem tree plantings in tropical and subtropical climates around the world.

These long-term plantations are expected to help solve global agricultural and health problems as well as provide income and sustainable job opportunities for rural and tribal communities. Indeed, the demand for Neem seeds for oil production is growing rapidly, as is the export market for other Neem materials.

 The use of Neem products in organic farming is steadily on the rise as more people across the globe are searching for clean foods and alternatives to harmful synthetic toxic chemicals. This demand has increased prices for raw Neem products and is resulting in higher wages being paid to the village laborers who collect Neem fruits. In the past nine years these laborer's wages have grown five-fold.

This demand has also increased Neem harvests that were previously restricted to the southern states of India, but now include harvesting Neem from across the Indian subcontinent.

The use of Neem in the agricultural sector is expected to increase substantially as various state governments in India have started promoting the use of Neem by distributing Neem cake and bio-pesticides through government sponsored schemes for farmers.

Exciting prospects are emerging for the use of Neem in health care. As recent studies suggest, Neem may be an effective treatment for cancer, gastric disorders, skin diseases and even HIV/AIDS. [55]

The increased demand of Neem products is expected to put pressure on the availability and supply of raw Neem materials. Since Indian supply and labor is limited, it may be necessary to open up other areas for Neem production to supply the expanding global market. This is now occurring with Brazil, and China emerging as major Neem producers.

On this, and previously mentioned topics, I have included for the reader Dr Saxena's article in its entirety with permission.

Neem for Sustainable Development and Environmental Conservation:

An Indian Perspective

By: Dr. Ramesh C. Saxena

---

[55] Mbah, A. U., Udeinya, I. J., Shu, E. N., Chijioke, C. P., Nubila, T., Udeinya, F., ... & Obioma, M. S. (2007). Fractionated neem leaf extract is safe and increases CD4+ cell levels in HIV/AIDS patients. *American journal of therapeutics*, *14*(4), 369-374.

The population of India has already crossed the one billion mark. Providing adequate food entitlements, safeguarding public health, meeting fuel and firewood needs, and at the same time preventing deforestation and conserving the environment, and slowing down the population growth will be daunting challenges in the coming decades.

Although "green revolution technologies" have more than doubled the yield potential of cereals, especially rice and wheat in India, these high - input production systems requiring large quantities of fertilizers, pesticides, irrigation, and machines, disregard the ecological integrity of land, forests, and water resources, endanger the flora and fauna, and cannot be sustained over generations.

Future food security and economic development would depend on improving the productivity or biophysical resources through the application of sustainable production methods, by improving tolerance of crops to adverse environmental conditions, and by reducing crop and post-harvest losses caused by pests and diseases.

Appropriate technologies, which do not assault nature, would have key roles to play in ensuring food security, in improving public and animal health, and in rehabilitating the environment to safeguard its well being. The future must look to natural ways and process for augmenting agricultural productivity. In fact, all development efforts and activities, including pest management, should be within well-defined ecological rules rather than within narrow economic gains.

Sustainable agricultural systems must be efficient (i.e. effective and economically rewarding) and ecologically sound for long-term food sufficiency, equitable in providing social justice, ethical in respecting both future generations and other species, and also lead to employment and income-generating opportunities. For India, the use of neem may provide a key component in ensuring sustainable agricultural systems, including pest and nutrient management, animal health, human health, and environmental conservation.

Neem, a member of the Meliaceae family, is a botanical cousin of mahogany. According to a report of an ad hoc panel of the Board on Science and Technology for International Development, "this plant may usher in a new era in pest control, provide millions with inexpensive medicines, cut down the rate of human population growth and even reduce erosion, deforestation, and the excessive temperature of an overheated globe."

Neem's other descriptions, such as "nature's gift to mankind," "the tree for many an occasion," " the tree that purifies," " the wonder tree," "the tree of the 21st century," and "a tree for solving global problems," are a recognition of its versatility. Its botanic name, Azadirachta indica, derived from Farsi, "azad darakht i hindi" literally means the "free or noble tree of India," suggesting that it is intrinsically free from pest and disease problems and is benign to the environment.

Neem is an evergreen, tall, fast-growing tree, which can reach a height of 25m and 2.5m in girth. It has an attractive crown of deep green foliage and masses of honey scented flowers. A full-grown tree can produce 30 to 100 kg of fruits, depending on rainfall, insolation, soil type, and ecotype. 50 kg of fruit yields 30 kg of seed, which gives 6 kg of oil and 24 kg of seed cake.

Neem has more than 100 unique bio-active compounds, which have potential applications in agriculture, animal care, public health, and even for regulating human fertility.

Neem has had a long history of use primarily against household and storage pests and to some extent against crop pests in India. With the advent of broad-spectrum, toxic insecticides, such as DDT, the use of neem in crop protection declined. However, over the past two decades, neem has come under close scientific scrutiny as a source of unique natural products for

IPM, medicine, industry, and other purposes. In spite of high selectivity, neem derivatives affect 400 to 500 species of mites and ticks, nematodes, and even noxious snails and fungi, and aflatoxin - producing Aspergillus spp.

Results of large-scale field trials conducted by me and others have illustrated the value of neem-based pest management for enhancing agricultural productivity. The use of neem and fertilizer mixtures can reduce ammonia volatilization loss caused by nitrifying bacteria in soil, thus effecting saving on fertilizers. A large number of neem-based medicines, pharmaceuticals, and toiletries are being produced today and are in great demand overseas.

Neem has scope in reforestation and agro forestry and rehabilitating wasted and degraded lands. It is useful as windbreaks and in areas of low rainfall and high wind speed; it can protect crops from desiccation.

Neem has much to offer in solving agricultural and public health problems in the country, especially in rural areas. However, more neem trees will have to be grown to meet the increasing demand for insecticidal and industrial uses.

The local peasant community will have to be brought within the fold of increased awareness by outreaching and through interpersonal interaction, by involving 'sarpanch' or village chiefs, schools, women groups, and government and non-government organizations. Field demonstrations and neem fairs at strategic locations will have to be organized periodically in collaboration with local bodies or institutions to evoke the interest and participation of target communities. Also, existing local initiatives, if any, will have to be strengthened.

Strategies for creating awareness will involve hands-on training through lectures and demonstrations to trainers, comprising agricultural trainers, foresters, extension personnel, health workers, teachers, journalists, and representatives of NGOs, youth and women groups, who would then have a multiplier effect in target areas. They will have to be taught how to harvest, collect and process neem seed, grow and plant seedling, and use various neem materials for pest management. The distribution of raw materials will have to be guaranteed by establishing nodal agencies in target areas. These activities will create employment opportunities and also generate income.

The complex molecular structure of bio-active neem compounds precludes their chemical synthesis economically. Therefore, even the chemical industry will have to rely on the use of raw material.

With growing demand for natural pest control materials, the use of neem products is becoming popular worldwide. In the next decade, it is expected that global neem trade, comprising neem-based pest control materials, medicines, pharmaceuticals, and toiletries will grow to more than $500m.

Herein lies a huge window of opportunity to benefit by growing and harnessing neem not only for local use but also for export to regions and countries where neem does not thrive.

Ramesh Saxena

Chairman at Neem Foundation

Gurgaon, IndiaEnvironmental Services

International Center for Insect Physiology and Ecology (ICIPE), International Rice Research Institute (IRRI)

Education:

Govt College, Nainital, University of Hawaii, Honolulu, USA; Delhi University, Delhi, India.

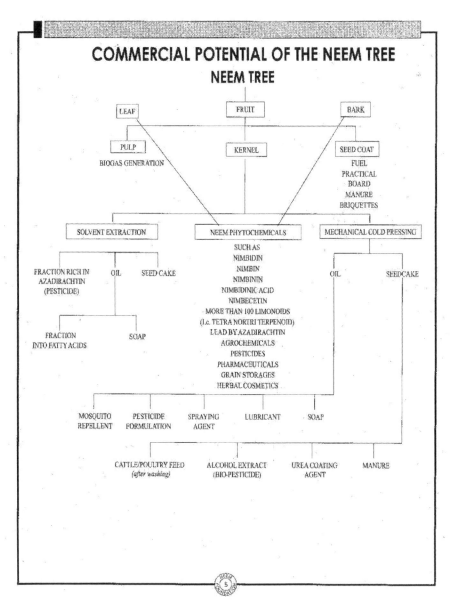

Graph courtesy of the Neem Foundation.

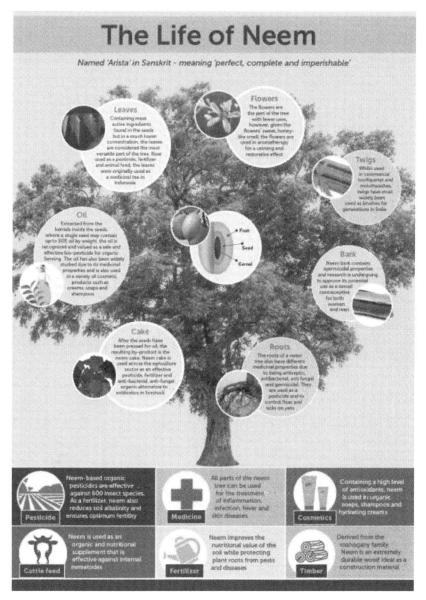

The Life of Neem (courtesy of www.primalgroup.com)

The Neem Tree - A Study

It is time that we turn towards Mother Nature and the Neem tree
that offers better plant health, human health, animal
health and environmental health

Dr Saxena

An academic study of the Neem tree is presented in this chapter in its entirety, including references, with permission from its author, Dr Ramesh Saxena.

The Neem Tree: Its Geographic Distribution, Plantation Characteristics, Growth and Yield, Genetic Variation, and Associated Pests and Diseases [56]

R. C. SAXENA [57]

Chairman, Neem Foundation
G=152, Palam Vihar, Gurgaon 122017, Haryana, India

---

[56] Presented at a Neem Training Workshop held at Kunming City, Yunnan Province, PROC, 6-8 Nov 2001.

[57] E-mail: susaxena@satyam.net.in

The Neem tree, a botanical cousin of mahogany (Meliaceae), is a fascinating tree. According to a report by the ad-hoc panel of the Board on Science and Technology for International Development appointed by the National Research Council, Washington, DC: "this plant may usher in a new era in pest control, provide millions with inexpensive medicines, cut down the rate of human population growth, and reduce erosion, deforestation, and the excessive temperature of an overheated globe."

These attributes have been aptly described in the book "Neem – A Tree for Solving Global Problems," published by the National Research Council (1992).

Neem's other descriptions, such as "nature's bitter boon," "nature's gift to mankind," "the tree for many an occasion," the tree that purifies," "the wonder tree," and "the tree of the 21st century," are recognition of its value and versatility.

Its botanical name, Azadirachta indica, derived from Farsi "azad dirakhta-i-hind," literally means "noble/free tree of the Indian sub-continent," suggesting that it intrinsically frees one from diseases. Neem's Sanskritized name, "Aristha," means the reliever of sickness. In Kiswahili, neem has come to be known as "Mwarubaini," meaning reliever of 40 common disorders.

Fig. 1. Previous page. Neem is now widespread in arid and semi-arid regions of Africa, but lack of awareness of its potential led someone to fell a full-grown tree (foreground), which could have been a rich source of novel, natural pest control materials and other useful products (Photograph by R.C. Saxena.)

The antiquity of neem is uncertain, although it is reported that a leaflet of neem was found fossilized in earth mines of Eocene period in Rajasthan, India (Mitra 1962). Emperor Asoka was one of the earliest to recognize the value of neem as a shade and avenue tree. Presently, neem is widely cultivated in arid, semi-arid, wet tropical, and sub-tropical regions of the Indian subcontinent. Such a wide adaptation and tolerance to varied soil and climatic conditions are a testimony to neem's resilience and versatility.

Geographic Distribution

Neem is thought to have originated in Burma and is common throughout the open scrub forests in the dry zone on the Siwalik hills. According to Ahmed and Grainge (1985), neem is native to the Indo-Pakistan subcontinent. Others attribute its nativity to the dry forest areas of India, Pakistan, Sri Lanka, Malaysia, Indonesia, Thailand, and Burma.

Sabena (unpublished) has identified more than 30 names of need in vernacular languages and more than 100 ethno-medicinal uses of neem in India, lending support to its Indian nativity. The commercial use of neem was known in India over 4000 years BC. Kautilya in his 'Arthashastra' has also mentioned the domestic uses of neem in the 4th century BC.

In its native environment, neem is generally found growing in mixed forests, and associated with other broadleaf species, such as Acacia spp. and Dalbergia sisso. It grows in tropical to subtropical regions, semi-arid to wet tropical regions; and from sea level to over 600 m (Benge 1989). It is grown throughout India, and in many places has become wild. Birds and bats consume the sweet pericarp of the fruit and are mainly responsible for the spread of wild neem. It is now found in many places outside its native distribution to the sub-Himalyan region, including the northern part of Uttar Pradesh at 600 m and the southern part of Kashmir at 700 m.

Contrary to the popular belief that neem does not grow at altitudes of 700 m and above, in Kenya, neem seedlings planted at altitudes of up to 1500 m in the equatorial belt, are thriving; a testimony to its hardiness. Of course, neem does not tolerate long cold spells and frost.

Indian immigrants introduced neem to Mauritius and also to a number of African countries. It is now abundant in the tropical belt from Somalia in the east to Mauritania in the West. It was also taken to Fiji Islands and from there has spread to other islands in the South Pacific.

Neem is reported to occur in Trinidad and other West Indian Islands and also in several countries of Central and Southern America. In the 1980s, RC Saxena, then at the International Rice Research Institute (IRRI), and a few scientists attached to the German Society for Technical Co-operation (GTZ) in the Philippines promoted large-scale planting of neem in the Philippines. Large-scale neem plantations have also come up in Malaysia. About a decade ago, the neem tree was chosen for large-scale planting on the plains of Arafat, near Mecca, for providing shade to pilgrims. Fifty thousand neem trees, spread over 10 km2, now adorn the once barren sands at Arafat (Ahmed et al. 1989).

Saxena (1993) constructed a world map showing the geographic origin of neem, introductions as of 1984, and the recent introductions (Fig. 2). Today, neem is the most sought after tree species for planting in tropical parts of countries as far as Australia to the USA.

Since the start of the ICIPE-Finland-UNEP Neem Awareness Project in 1994, neem has been widely planted in Kenya, Uganda, and Tanzania, and other neighboring countries. For instance, more than 200,000 neem trees were grown in pure stands and in mixed plantations at Adjumani, northern Uganda. Likewise, in the Kwimba Reforestation Project, Mwanza, Tanzania, more than 600,000 neem trees were planted on homesteads and in plantations.

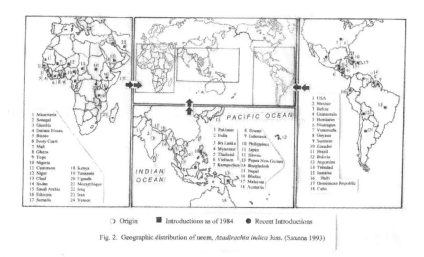

Fig. 2. Geographic distribution of neem, *Azadirachta indica* Juss. (Saxena 1993)

Fig. 2. Geographic distribution of neem, Azadirachta indica Juss. Saxena (1993) Schmutterer (1995) has compiled detailed information on the geographic distribution of neem in the world today:

Australia and South Pacific. In the last century, indentured labourers and immigrants from India introduced neem in the western parts of Viti Levu (Sigatoka velley) in Fiji Islands. In the past decade, neem was planted in small stands on several islands of the Hawaiian archipelago, including the big island, Hawaii. From 1982 onwards, neem was planted in the Markham valley and in Port Moresby area in Papua New Guinea; the other regions with high rainfall were not suitable for neem. In Australia, more than 150,000 neem trees have been planted in the Northern Territory and northern Queensland in the past 10 years.

Southeast Asia and South China. Neem has been grown in eastern parts of Java and in islands east of Java. But it is missing on Sumatra and Borneo (Kalimantan). In Malaysia, Indian immigrants introduced neem early in the

20th century. It occurs in scattered patches on the peninsula. Neem is more common in the Northern provinces Perlis and Kedah and quite abundant in George Town on the Penang Island and in Butterworth east of it. In Thailand, neem occurs in scattered lots in southern and central parts of the country. Neem, A. indica ('Sadao India'), characterized by white flushing inflorescence, is generally seen near pagodas and was most probably introduced by Buddhist monks for phyto-medicinal purposes. The Thai neem, Azadirachta siamensis (Val.) ('Sadao Thai') with red inflorescence, earlier considered as a variety of A. indica, has recently been categorized as a different species. 'Sadao Thai' grows wild and is distributed throughout Thailand below 200-m altitude within a well-defined boundary towards west and north, extending to Cambodia and Laos. Natural hybrids between 'Sadao India' and 'Sadao Thai' have been observed in the southern peninsula, but not in the north because of differences in the time of flowering.

Since about 1984, as a result of RC Saxena's initiative and GTZ program, large-scale planting of neem has taken place in Luzon, Visayas, and Mindanao in the Philippines. Planting of neem was hampered in the northern and central parts of the archipelago due to frequent typhoons, high rainfall, and some diseases, but growth in low-lying regions of Mindanao and Palawan was normal.

In South China, neem was introduced on the Hainan Peninsula about 10 years ago. Neem is now being planted on a large scale in Yunnan province. A small experimental plantation has been established near Da Nang in Vietnam.

South Asia. Neem is thought to have originated in upper Myanamar (Burma). It is common in central regions south of Mandalay, but is rare in humid southern parts of the country. A few scattered neem trees occur in the southern regions of Nepal, but central and northern regions are unsuitable for neem due to high altitude and cold weather. Neem is common in central parts of Bangladesh. Neem occurs in the wild in Siwalik hills, in forests of Karnataka, and in parts of Deccan, indicating that India can be a probable place of origin. It is very common in most tropical and sub-tropical parts and the total number exceeds 20 M in India. Uttar Pradesh (northern province), followed by Tamil Nadu, has the largest number of neem trees in India. Bahraich district in northeastern U.P. has probably the largest and oldest plantation in the world.

In Sri Lanka, neem occurs mainly in northern regions; central highlands are unsuitable for neem cultivation due to high altitude. Neem is common in southern and central parts of Pakistan. In Iran, neem occurs in parks and settlements along the coast up to the Chat el Arab.

Middle East. Neem has been planted under irrigation in towns in Oman and Qatar as an ornamental. Also, it is common in Mekkah and Medinah, particularly on the plains of Arafat.

Africa. Neem is common in Toliara and villages around it in the southwestern parts of Madagascar. The highlands and eastern and central regions are unsuitable due to high altitude and high rainfall. Neem is a popular tree in Mauritius, particularly in coastal regions.

Neem is scattered throughout East Africa Somalia, Kenya, Tanzania, and Uganda. In Somalia, neem was planted in the past 20 years. It is a common shade tree in Mogadishu and other towns of the southern parts. In Kenya, it is scattered in and around coastal Kenya: Mombasa, Malindi, Lamu, etc. It also occurs in Wajjir and Garissa in the northeast part of the country. In Tanzania, it is very common on Zanzibar and Pemba islands and has also been planted in considerable numbers in the area between

Tanga and Moshi and in Mwanza province. In Uganda, neem is scattered in Adjumani (northern Uganda near the Sudanese border).

In Southeast Africa (Zimbabwe, Malawi, Mozambique), scattered neem trees are seen in northern parts near human settlements. Southern parts are generally unsuitable due to low temperatures during winter months. However, a few trainees trained in the ICIPE-Finland-UNEP Neem Awareness Project are attempting to introduce neem in northern regions of Southeast Africa.

In Ethiopia, neem is growing well in Awash valley and the Dire Dawa region. In Sudan, foresters introduced neem in 1921. It is growing abundantly in towns and villages along Blue and White Niles and in Kordofan Province in the west.

In West Africa (northern Cameroon, Nigeria, Benin, Togo, Ghana, Ivory Coast), neem is very common mainly in the northern regions of these countries. In Nigeria, it was introduced in 1928 and is called 'Baba Yaro.' It is planted in large numbers as an avenue tree between Maiduguri and Lake Chad. Small plantations of neem have been established in Burkina Faso during the past 15 years. In Ghana, Sir Frederick Guggisberg introduced it from India during 1919–1927. The tree is called 'King' in Ghana. In Mali, neem is known as 'goo-ga' after Sir Guggisberg.

In Niger, 'green belts' of neem trees have been established around Niamey and also several miles long neem windbreaks have been created in the Majjia Valley and other regions. In Mali, neem is a part of the scene along the Niger River as far north as Timbuktu.

Neem is very common in Senegal and Gambia, and found practically in almost every human settlement, even in remote areas. Senegal alone has probably more than 5 million full grown neem trees.

In Mauritania, neem is scattered in the southwestern parts, especially in Nagichot.

A few neem trees are growing in the Central Park of Las Palmas in Gran Canaria (Canarian Islands, Spain).

The Americas. Apparently, Indian immigrants introduced neem to several Caribbean nations. Neem is now grown as a medicinal plant in Suriname, Gyuana, Trinidad and Tabago, Barbados, Jamaica, and elsewhere. Recently, neem has also been introduced in Cuba, St. Lucia, Antigua, Dominican Republic, Mexico, Panama, Belize, Guatemala, Honduras, Nicaragua, Bolivia,

Ecuador, Brazil, and Venezuela. Large neem plantations have been established in Haiti in the past two decades.

In the USA, a few neem trees are thriving in Florida. Efforts are underway to promote neem plantings in southern California, Arizona, and Oklahoma.

Plantation Characteristics

In its native environment, neem is generally found in mixed forests. However, little is known about the behavior of neem in plant communities. Individual trees are known to survive more than 200 years and thrive better when grown on isolated basis than in full groves. It grows beautifully along roadsides. Many roads in New Delhi are lined by stately neem trees, which are more than 100 years old.

Growth and Yield

Neem is a fast grower, but growth depends on edaphic factors (environment and site characteristics) and on plant ecotype or genotype. Growth is slower in cooler areas and at higher altitudes. Radwanski (1977) reported that neem reaches a height of 4 -7 m in the first 3 years and 5 to 11 m in the following 5 years. Generally, neem trees put on a mean-annual girth of 10-20 cm, but growth is more rapid in favorable environments. In India, neem trees are known to reach diameters of over 40 cm in 16 years. In Africa, in 1 year in good soil, the tree reaches a height of 1.5 m, at 2 years a height of 2 m. At Mbita in western Kenya, a 4- to 5-year-old neem trees attains a diameter of 15-20 cm. Weeds and grasses hamper early growth of neem. Well-weeded neem seedlings grow much faster.

 The yield of neem varies from 10-100 tons of dried biomass/ha/year, depending on the rainfall, site conditions, and spacing and 40 tons (12.5 m3 solid wood/ ha/ year) can be obtained easily under proper conditions. Leaves comprise about 50% of the biomass, wood ca. 25%, and fruit about 25%.

Genetic Variation

Little information exists on genetic variation or on provenances of neem. Neem was introduced in the past with little regard to seed-origins. Tree to tree and provenance variation both within a region and between different regions, therefore, needs to be studied. Land races and taxonomic varieties of neem, where they exist, need to be identified, collected, and evaluated.

Neem has been widely planted in different climatic zones in India and used by Indians since antiquity. Introductions are so old that wide that our knowledge of its wild distribution has become uncertain. However, for breeding and collection of neem germplasm, the genetic variation needs to be determined because seed sources from wild range are genetically diverse and valuable. Neem provenances collected from eastern semi-arid to western extremely arid range of Rajasthan desert vary in adaptability from moist to extreme arid regions (Dogra and Thapliyal 1993). Selection from this range may provide highly desert-adapted superior fodder producing germplasm. Neem provenances from Lucknow to eastern Indian regions receiving more rainfall vary greatly in tree form and size than those from arid regions. The seed origins of India and its adjacent regions are therefore valuable for tree improvement work.

Recent neem introductions in different regions of Africa are likely to have a narrow genetic base and a narrow adaptability as natural selection in these areas has occurred only for a short duration and on a very narrow genetic base.

Differences in azadirachtin content from seed origins have been recorded from different geographic regions. Ermel (1995) evaluated 256 samples from 22 countries. The highest azadirachtin content (0.514 – 0.610%) was found in samples from south and Southeast Asia (India, Myanmar, and Thailand), while below average (0.360%) azadirachtin was measured in samples from countries with extremely high temperatures during summer months (Sudan, Somalia, Mali, Niger, etc.). Samples collected from the Caribbean showed intermediate azadirachtin content. Gupta et al. (1997) reported that maximum azadirachtin content (0.617%) was found in neem seed kernel from Yezin (Myanmar) and least (0.113% in seed kernel from Chapai Nwabganj (Bangladesh). In India, neem seed kernel from Orissa had 0.483% azadirachtin, while that from Rajasthan had 0.404% azadirachtin. There was no correlation between seed size, seed weight, fatty oil content and azadirachtin content with respect to regions of collection. Maximum azadirachtin content is recorded when neem fruits turn from green to yellow (Ravindranath 1997). It appears that beside genotypic variation, edaphic factors may also influence the azadirachtin content in neem seed.

Pest, Diseases, and Other Constraints

Neem has few pests and is not vulnerable to common diseases unless grown in unnatural, stressed environments. However, a few organisms have adapted themselves to neem over thousands of years of co-evolution. For instance, some species of snails have been found to cause heavy damage to seedlings in nurseries in Cuba and Australia. Likewise, some spider mites and gall mites can attack young leaves of seedlings when grown in crowded conditions. Occasional infestations by Microtermes spp., and plant parasitim by Lorantium have been observed in Nigeria, but the trees readily recover. When neem is too much water-stressed, then the yellow oriental scale insect, Aonidiella orientalis, has been known to damage neem trees in some parts of Africa, e.g. the Lake Chad Basin in Niger, Chad, and Cameroon. In India, larvae of Enarmonia koenigana feed on rolled leaves and bore into tender shoots. Likewise, larvae of Cleora cornaria and Odites atmopa can defoliate the leaves. A few other insects can attack neem, but rarely an old tree dies due to insect attack. In South India, the tea mosquito bug Helopeltis antonii can damage young shoots and leaves, but only the affected branch dries up. A few soft- and armored scales (Homoptera) are found on neem, but do not cause any significant damage. Leaf-cutting ants, Atta spp. and Acromyrmes spp. can attack young neem trees in central and southern America. These ants in Cuba, Ecuador and Venezuela have reportedly caused heavy damage to young neem plants. A beetle, the black borer, Apate monachus, is known to attack shoots, young branches, and stems of young neem plants in the

Caribbean and occasionally in West Africa. The infested shoots break and dry up, but damaged plants regenerate quickly. Occasional defoliation of neem by some species of curculionids and scarabeid beetles has been reported in India, but the trees fully recover soon.

Several bird species, such as starlings and ravens, feed on the pulp of neem fruits, but the seed remains undamaged. In fact, the birds may be regarded useful in the dispersal of neem in the wild. Likewise, flying foxes (fruit-eating bats) feed on neem fruits at night and help in disseminating neem in Africa. Goats have a predilection for neem leaves and can menace young plants during scarcity of food. Consequently, young plants have to be fenced in the African Savannah. In Senegal, goats feed even on neem fruits and seed lying on the ground, probably to get rid of internal parasites.

The saw-toothed grain beetle, Oryzaephilus surinamensis, is the most common pest of poorly stored, broken neem seed, but seed kernels in intact shell are not damaged. The corn sap beetle, Carpophilus dimidiatus, reportedly damaged stored neem seed in Ecuador, but this insect also is unable to penetrate and damage kernel in intact shell of neem seeds.

Neem seedlings, raised in crowded conditions, are known to become vulnerable to a few bacteria, especially Pseudomonas and Xanthomonas spp., in India. But seedlings grown under conditions of high rainfall or high humidity in Asia, becomes vulnerable to Rizoctonia disease caused by the fungus Rhizoctonia solani. In Australia, a species of Phellinus was found to damage roots of neem trees grown in alluvial soils and the trees severely infected died.

In coastal Kenya, the semi-parasitic plant Cassytha filiformis is causing some concern. Heavy infestation of small and medium-sized neem trees may lead to their destruction. However, the problem can be overcome by pruning of branches of infested trees and improved sanitation.

Aspergillus flavus may build-up in poorly handled neem fruit and seed and may pose a health hazard. The harvested fruit therefore must be de-pulped quickly, and the washed seed surface sterilized and dried thoroughly before storing.

Ramesh Saxena
Chairman at Neem Foundation
Gurgaon, IndiaEnvironmental Services
International Center for Insect Physiology and Ecology (ICIPE), International Rice Research Institute (IRRI)
Education
Govt College, Nainital, University of Hawaii, Honolulu, USA; Delhi University, Delhi, India

References

Ahmed, S. and M. Grainge. 1985. The use of indigenous plant resources in rural development: Potential of the neem tree. Int. J. Dev. Tehnol. 3: 123.

Ahmed, S., S. Bamofleh, and M. Munshi. 1989. Cultivation of neem (Azadirachta indica Meliaceae) in Saudi Arabia. Econ. Bot. 43: 34-38.

Benge, M. 1986. Neem: The Cornucopia Tree. S & T/FENR Agro-Forestation Technical Ser. No. 5. Agency for International Development, Washington DC

Dogra, P. D. and R. C. Thapliyal. 1993. Gene resources and breeding potential, pp. 27-32. In N. S. Randhawa and B. S. Parmar (eds.), Neem Research and Development. Society of Pesticide Science, India.

Ermel, K. 1995. Azadirachtin content of neem seed kernels from different regions of the world, pp. 89-92. In H. Schmutterer (ed.), The Neem Tree: Azadirachta indica A. Juss. And Other Meliaceous Plants: Source of Unique Natural Products for Integrated Pest Management, Medicine, Industry and Other Purposes. VCH, Weinheim.

Gupta, P. K., Y. C. Tripathi, and R. S. Pal. 1997. Variation of fatty oil and azadirachtin contents of neem seed kernels of different geographical origins, pp. 142-148. In B. N. Gupta and K. K. Sharma (eds.), Neem – A Wonder Tree. Indian Council of Forestry Research and Education, Dehradoon, India.

Mitra, C. R. 1962. Melia. Bull. National Botanic Gardens 59, Lucknow, India.

National Research Council. 1992. Neem – A Tree for Solving Global Problems. National Academy Press, Washington, DC.

Radwanski, S. A. 1977. Neem tree. I. Commercial potential, characteristics, and distribution. World Crops Livestock 29: 62.

Ravindranath, B. 1997. Some recent advances in the chemistry, biology and technology of neem, pp. 139-141. In B. N. Gupta and K. K. Sharma (eds.), Neem – A Wonder Tree. Indian Council of Forestry Research and Education, Dehradoon, India.

Saxena, R. C. 1993. Neem as a source of natural insecticides - An update, pp. 1-24. In M. S. Chari and G. Ramaprasad (eds.), Botanical Pesticides in Integrated Pest Management. Proc. Nat'l Symposium held at Central Tobacco Research Institute, Rajahmundry, India Jan 1990.

Schmutterer, H. 1995. The tree and its characteristics, pp. 1-34. In H. Schmutterer (ed.), The Neem Tree: Azadirachta indica A. Juss. And Other Meliaceous Plants: Source of Unique Natural Products for Integrated Pest Management, Medicine, Industry and Other Purposes. VCH, Weinheim.

My Lovely Neem

My lovely Neem,

That intercepts sun's scorching beam,

Yet bears the heat all day

Without the rain's refreshing spray,

Thou charm'st the wanderer's woe away

With soothing shade.

How strong you are, how unafraid,

How green the leaves in spite of all

The mid-day flames that burning fall

Upon thy unprotected head...

Could man be as bold as thou and rise

Above the earth, with the sheltering arm

To save the suffering ones from harm,

From sorrows, poverty and vice

Through sacrifice.

Could man be steadfast, and like thee

Face every fate, would it not be

Fulfillment of life's loftiest dream

My lovely Neem!

- Elsa Kazi

The Lovely Village Neem Tree

Dr Joaquim Morgado MD with 220 year old Neem tree in Myanmar, 50meters high, with 40 meter wide crown. The UN declared Neem the tree of the 21ˢᵗ Century.

Neem Manufacturers, Distributors, Importers & Exporters

AFRICA

Cameroon
Aguti Cooperative, Panya 21 New Street, North West Region, Panya, Tel. 237-25374948, http://www.gmdu.net/corp-782165.html

Fako Fram Ltd, PO Box 12, Bafeya 00237, Tel. 237-238808, http://www.gmdu.net/corp-585174.html

Ghana
Acre Fresh Enterprise, PO Box CT 530, Cantonments, Tel. 233-208457842, http://www.acrefreshhllc.co.nr

Afra Medicinal Herbs Company, Teshie, Accra 00233, Tel. 233-246-320678, http://www.gh101674411.fm.alibaba.co

Kenya
Great O Lakes Company Ltd, PO Box 7715 – 00100, GPO, Nairobi, Tel. 254-735-677777, http://www.greatolakes.kbo.de

Mauritius
HKS Management Services Ltd, Nalletamby Road, Phoenix, Tel. 230-697-5369, http://www.mantra-ayur.com

Nigeria

Saberg International Ltd, Technology Incubation Center, TIC, Birmin Kebbi, Kebbi 800001, Tel. 234-068-322528, http://www.gmdu.net/corp-156963.html

Karamah Global Links, Lome Crescent, Kaduna 2739, Tel. 234-062-211372, http://www.gmdu.net/corp-450844.html

Jigna Eco Farms, Jigna Road, Abuja 234, Tel. 234-80-60555160, http://www.gmdu.net/corp-776654.html

South Africa

Absolute Neem Pvt Ltd, PO Box 159, West Coast Village, Western Cape, 7433, Tel. 27815720607. http://www.absoluteneem.com

Esoteric Oils, 359 Church Ave., Lynnwood 0081, Pretoria – City of Ishwane, Tel. 0027-1231-2112, http://www.essentialoils.co.za

The Himalayan Drug Company (Pty) Ltd, Yellow Wood Place, Woodmead Business Park, 145 Western Service Road, Woodmead 2191, Sandton, Postnet Suite 524, Private Bag X29, Gallo Manor, Johannesburg, 2052, Tel. 27 11 656 4284

Spice Emporium, 31 Monty Naicker Road, Durban 4001, Tel. 27-31332 5888, http://www.spiceemporium.co.za

Umuthi Essential Oils, PO Box 216, 747 North Street, Wilderness 6560, Tel. 044-8770372, http://www.essentialoilssouthafrica.co.za

ZMVULA Import & Export Pty Ltd, 9 Young Ave., Johannesburg, Tel. 27-621751441, http://www.ypbvtrustpass.alibaba.com

Sudan
Kordofal Taste Factory for Fruit Trees Extraction, PO Box 1546, Khartoum North 13311, Tel. 249-912-309750, http://www.kordofal.com

Togo
Ceam SARL, 104 Gbv, Rue Otowon Tokoin Gbonvie, Lome 9133500, Tel. 228-9133500, http://www.gmdu.net/corp-23144.html

Access Group, 14 Pk Rte. Anecho, Baguida, Lome 107, Tel. 228-904-1045, http://www.gumdu.net/corp-23369.html

Uganda
Neem Cosmetics Uganda Ltd, Plot 774 Bombo Road, Kawne Block 208, PO Box 31694, Kampala, Tel. 256-414-568-572, http://www.neemug.com

Uganda, Plot 483, Nabweru-Wakiso District, Wakiso 256, Tel. 256-785-884490, http://www.ng113002787fm.alibaba.com

ASIA

Bangladesh
Neem Laboratories (Pty) Ltd, House No. 497, Roadno 33, New Dohs, Mohakhali, Dhaka, Tel. 880-02-8856894, http://www.neemkimya.com

Agro All Arpnd Ltd, H-241, Road 3, Baridhara Dohs, Dhaka 1212, Tel. 880-2-8861627, http://www.asian-organic.com

The Muslim Herbal and Chemical Group of Industries Co., 61 Asam Coloy, Ghoramara, Jajshahi 6260, Tel. 880-0721-860269, htpp://www.bd1008688140.fm.alibaba.com

Naghma's Herbal Bangladesh, A-2, Peace Harbor, 63/3 Katashur, Dhaka 1207, Tel. 880-174-1363330, http://www.nagmasherbal.com

Agro All Around Ltd, Road#03, House #255. Dohs, Barid Hara, Dhaka 1206, Tel. 880-2-84-10026, http://www.bd104446332.fm.alibaba.com

Neem Laboratories (Pvt) Lltd, Houe No. 497, Road N. 33, New Dohs, Mohakhli, Dhaka 1206, Tel. 880-02-8856894, http://www.neembd.org

China

Yuannan Honghe Guanming Co. Ltd, Yuannan Guanming Neem Industries Development Co. Ltd, 120 Xinan Road, Kai Yuan, Yunann, PC, 661000, Tel. Mob: 013908847792 Fax: 86-873-7122528

Shaanix Longfu Biochemical Co. Ltd,Room 402, West Tower, Kaili Building, No. 8, Tech Road, Xian 710 065, Tel. 86-029-82097300, http://www.en.extract123.com

Xi'An Realin Biotechnology Co. Lld, Wangtingguijo 3-21706, No. 80 Gaoxin Road, Xian 710 065, Tel. 86-029-89382595, http://www.xarealin.com

Shanxi Pioneer Biotech Co. Ltd, Room 1905, Unit 1, Bldg. G1, Weilan Lingyu No. 11 Daqing Road, Lianhu District, Xi'an 710 065, Tel. 86-29-84385017, http://www.pioneertech.com

Xian Jiatian Biotec Co. Ltd, Floor 1, Unit 2, Building 5, Minjingyuan, ei Qu, Changian District, Xi'an 710100, Tel. 86-029-84191386, http://www.jatianbio.com

Beijing Packbury M & C Co Ltd, 1-1801 Cityscape Jiayuan Community, No. 123, Zhongguancun East Road, Haidian District, Beijing, Tel. 86-10-62191332, http://www.chinapackbury.com

Guangzhou Magnolia Cosmetics Co Ltd, Rm. 3332, No. 146, Huangbian North Road, Baiyun District. Guangzou, Guangdon 510000, Tel. 86-20-36164769, http://www.oemcosmetics.cn

Shanixi Gunjie Technology Co Lltd, Nol 11 Tangyan South Road, Xi'an 710065, Tel. 86-029-88253271, http://www.en.gybiotech.com

Shaanxi Fuhencfh Biotechnology Co. Ltd, 12 F Jierui Building, No. 208 South, Erhuan Road, Xi'an 710068, Tel. 86-29-88378803, http://www.xafhbio.com,

Shaanxi Rebecca Bio-Tech Co. Ltd, No. 12810, Building1, Xubaug Building, No. 13, Nonglin Lane, Chang'an Riad, Yanta District, Shaanix, Xi'an 710000, Tel. 86-29-852-19166, http://www.sxrebecca.com

Guangzhou Anarie Cosmetics Co Ltd, Room 465, No. 161, Tianfu Road, Tianhe, Tel. 86-20-38393919, http://www.amarrie.com

Shandong Quichang Chemical Co Ltd, No. 1181 Huanghe 12 Road, Shandong Province, Binzhou 256601, Tel. 86-543-2226170, http://www.sdqc.com.cn

Nanjing Zelang Technology Co Ltd, Nol 108, Ganjiabian,Qixia District Nanjing, Jiangsu, Nanjing 210046, Tel. 86-25-83269275, http://www.ze-pharm.com

Guangxi Nanning Guangtai Agriculture Chemical Co Lltd, Rm 703, Building 12, Software Park, Phse II, NO. 68, Keyuan Ave., Guangxi, Nanning 530007, Tel. 86-771-2311266, http://www.gtagro.cn

Yangzhou Getright Chemical Co. Ltd., Room 1003, Bldg. 5, Weixi, Garden, Kaifa Road, Hanjiang Area, Jiangsu, Yangzhou, Tel. 86-514-87922948, http://www.getright.en.alibaba.com

Shenzen Yufull Industries Co. Ltd, Room 2128- 2133, Wantong Building, No. 3002 East Sun Gang Road, Luohu District, Guangdon Province, Shenzen 518023, Tel. 86-755-25867955, http://www.yufull.com

Rely Chemicals Ltd, B1-1-1607, No. 180 Yuan Qian Road, Lianyungang 222042, Tel. 86-518-81061113 http://www.relychem.com

Naturalin Bio-Resoruces Co. Ltd, B1- 402, No. 27 Wenxuan Road, Changsha 410205, Tel. 86-731-84830167, http://www.naturalin.com

Guangzhou Hong Ji Hui Daliy Apppliance Co Ltd, Rm 601-611, No. Development Building, Denfgen Street, Llujing Road, Guangzhou, Te. 86-66317000, http://www.konjihui.com.cn

Sichuan Divineland Aute Agricltural Science Co Ltd, 7th Group, Huanghshi Village, Baima Town, Mid Dist. , Neijiang, Sichuan, Chengdu 610014, Tel. 86-028-86289011, http://www.aute.net.cn

Yiwu Bicooya Cosmetics Ltd, 502, Yuanda Zone, 428 Wenzhou Ave., Wenzhou 325000, Tel. 86-577-86356659, http://www.senosmarketing.com

Hong Kong

Y-Organic, Flat 1602, Block A, Ching Wang Court, Tsing YI, NT, Tel. 51102913, http://www.y-organic.com

Vantage Resources Ltd, Unit 24, 7th Floor, Shig Yip Industrial Building, 19-21 Shing Yip Street, Kwunton, Tel. 852-214-74120. http://www.vrl.hk

Yenchen Kuo, 33F-2, NO. 80 Min-Chin 1st Road, Kaoshiung, Tel. 886-939—802793, http://www.tw10144334-10.fm.alibaba.com

India

Agri Life Som Phytopharma (India) Limited, 154/AS SVCIE, Ida, Bollaram 502 325, Tel. 91-98854 46278, http://www.somphyto.com

Agro Extracts Limited, Plot No. 16, Peenya Industrial Area, Bangalore 560 058, Tel. +91-80-28397276 - +91-28397275, http://www.agroextracts.com

Ajay Bio-Ech (India) Ltd, 2, 1st Floor, Tara Icon, Pune-MUmbai Road, Wakdewadi, Pune 411 003, Tel. 91-020-323-09200, http://www.ajaybio.in

Cultivator Natural Products,Soamukhi Nagar, Sancaria Fanta, Jodhpur 342 005, Tel. 91-291-2764488, http://www.cultivator.in

Genera Nutrients Private Ltd, 37-B, Puthupalayam, Avalpoondurad Road, Erode 638 115, Tel. 91-7053120761,http://www.moringasuppliers.com

Green Earth Products, W-105, Greater Kailach, Part I, New Delhi 110 048, Tel. +91-(11) 8447565969, http://www.greenearthproducts.net

Greenvalley xim India, Jl Raya 88, Jakarta 11530, Tel. 62-4252-227950, http://www.thangaray.fm.alibaba.com

The Himalaya Drug Company, Makali, Bangalore 562 162, Tel. 91-80 2371 444, http://www.himalayawellness.com,

Jain Group of Industries, 46, Sector -7A, Faridabad 121 006 , Tel. 91-120-2241531, http://www.jain-group.com

Indeneed Corporation, Kavery Complex Kovundampalayam Nallampalayam Road, Coimbatore 641 030, Tel. +91-8447526625, http://www.ajaybio.in

Mani Dharma Biotec Pvt Ltd, No. 61, Kamatchi Nagar, Madanandhapurham, Chennai 600 125, Tel. 91-988-4848219, http://www.manidharmabiotech.com

Nature Neem Products, No. 10, State Bank Colony, Samanthana Puran, Rayapuram Extension, Tirupur, 641 601, Tel. +91-984-3612239, http://www.natureneem.com

Neem India, Siddharth Acrace, Railway Station Road, Aurangabad 431 005, Tel. 91-240-235 4912-17, http://www.neemindia.com

Neemtek Organic Producers Ltd, No. 14, 4th East Main Road, Gandhinagar, Katpadi, Vellore, Tel. 91-0416-291-5252, http://www.gmdu.net/corp-744877.html

Nico Orgo Manures, Opp Railway Station, Dakor 388 225, Tel. +91-2699-24403, 244611, http://www.neemnico.com

Ozone Biotech, Plot 6, 14/3, Mathura Road, Faridabad, Haryana 121003, Tel. 91-129-4196800, http://www.ozonebiotech.com

Organic India Pvt. Ltd, Plot No. 266, Faizabad Road, Kamta, Post Chinhat, Lucknow 227105, Tel. 81 (0) 522-2701579 http://www.organicindia.com

Parker Biotech Private Limited, No. 56-A Vasudevan Nagar, Jafferkhanpet, Chennai 600 083, +91-44-657625 +91-44-421-4590, http://www.organicneem.com

Pradeep Agro Tec (Pvt) Ltd Kadlas, Tal savigola, Dist. Solapur, Solapur, Maharashtra 413309, Tel. 91-2187-247206, http://www.kadlasneemindia.com

Prithvi Exports, A3/29, Vridavan, Dongre Park Society, Mumbai 400074, Tel. 91-9833275725, http://www.prithviexports.in

Pioneer Enterprise, Vatsalya B Co-Op HSG Ltd, 33-33A Sant Savta Marg, NO. 3, Opp. Nariel Wadi, Mazgoan, Mumbai, 400 010, Tel. +91-33-23757188, +91-22-23757189, http://www.pioneerherbal.com

RYM Exports, 23, Anuradha Society, Old Nagardas Road, Andheri (E), Mumbai 400 069, Tel. =91-22-32956539, http://www.naturalproducts-india.com

Sumukha Farm Products Pvt Ltd., No. 12/8, 9, Senthil Complex, BSNL Office Road, Indira Nagar Hosur, 635 109, Tel. +91-4344-243647, 91+-9953353163, http://www.nutriline.in

Sun Tower, Supeer A-7, Tuk Industrial Estate, Guindy, Chennai 600 032,

Tel. 91-44-43552518, http://www.organic-neem.com

Terramera BioSciences India Private Limited, NO. 302 FM House, Anna Salai, Tenampet, Chennai 600006, http://www.plasmaneem.com

The Indian Neem Tree Comapny, M/S RYM Exporters, 23 Anuradha Society, Old Nagardas Road, Andhri (E), Mumbai 400 069, Tel. +91-22 329 56 539, +91-2821 0025, http://www.neemtreeindia.com

Uno Natural & Greens Pvt Ltd, W-822, 9th Street, Syndicate Colony, Anna Nagar, WE, Chennai 600 101, Tel. 91-8587892230, http://www.unonaturalgreens.com

Vana Shree Agriculture Pvt Ltd, Vishnu Najan, J-116 Mega Center, Margarpatta Socapur Road, Hadapsar, Pune 411 028, Tel.. 91-9953353430, http://www/vanashreegrotech.com

Vnet Agrochemicals, Gangotri Complex, Mayfair Road, B/H Central Bank, Anand 388 001, Tel. 91-2692645832, http://www.vnetagrochemicals.com

SPS Organics India Private Ltd, S No. 123/ 6C3, Pichampalayam, P Mettur, P.O. Mallur, Salem 636 203, Tel. 91-9953364275, http://www.neemproducts.in

Nepal
Nepal Sanjiwani Herbal Industry & Bubbles International (P) Ltd, Shrish Marg, Kathmandu 32, Tel. 977-1-9841302141, http://www.snjiwaniherbal.com.np

Indonesia

Pt. Intaran Indonesia, Jl Mertasari Gg Sunrise School No. 01, Kerobktan Kuta, Denpasar, Bali 80361, Tel. 62-361-775822, http://www.indoneem.com

Ichimaru Pharlos Co. Ltd, 318-1-Asagi, Motosu-Shi 501 – 0475, Tel. 81-58-3201032, http://www.ichimaru.j

PT Intaran Indonesia, JL Mertasari Gg Sunrise School 01, Kerobokan 80361, Tel. 62-361-735822, http://www.indoneem.com

Paradise Fashion, Jl Petitenget, Gang Cendrawasih 2, Krobokan, Bali 80361, Tel. 62-361-736440, http://www.gmdu.net/corp-275156.html

Japan
Ichimaru Pharcos Co Ltd, 318-1 Asagi, Motosu-Shi, Tel. 81-58-3201032, http://www.ichimaron.co.jp

Malaysia
Big Corp – A Berhad, 135-SS171/A, Subang Jaya 47500, Tel. 60-03-5637555, http://www.litna.com

HigaTech Progress, Sdn Bhd 144-O, Jalan Kotalaksamana – 9, Taman, Melaka 75200, Tel. 60-6-2842967, http://www.hitechprogress.fm.alibaba.com

Myanmar
Magt, 380 Bogyoke Aung San Road, Yangon 11141, Tel. 95-9-36077040, http://www.spa.myanmar.com

TT Whole Sale, 6/898 Byamaso Road, South Okkalapa TSP, Yangon 11162, Tel. 95-9-31581679, http://www.mm100385289.fm.alibaba.com

Pakistan

Quality Brands, 270/1 – C, DHA, Phase 4, Lahore 00000, Tel. 92-300-8732003, http://www.qualitybrands.com.pk

Faida Enterprises, 53 – Alitown, Raiwind Road, Lahore 54000, Tel. 92-321-4020784, http://www.faida.trustpass.alibaba.ccom

Phytomedix Nutra Chemicals, Plot No. 3 Main Jail Road PIBC, Karachi 74800, Tel. 92-21-34943440, http://www.phytomedix.com

Al – Marryan International, A/1284, Main Market Road, Hyderabad 71000, Tel. 92-22-2633263, http://www.almarryamist.com

The Planner Herbal Int., 208 Sabrina Center, Karachi 74200, Tel. 92-021-4249097, http://www.tphint.com

Philippines

Herbs and Healing, Loma De gato, Marilao, Tel. 63-923-1885295, http://www..alibaba.com

Herbs and Healing, Loma De gato, Marilao, Bulacan,Tel. 63-923-1885295, http://www.gmdu.net/corp-798494.html

Singapore

The Himalaya Drug Company Pvt Ltd, 9 Temasek Boulevard, #24-01 Suntec Tower 2, Singapore,038989, Tel. 65 6 5353067

Sri Lanka

Neemlanka (Pvt) Ltd, 444/11 Pitakotte, Kotte, Tel. 94-112-873312, http://www.neemgrolanka.com

Herbal Exotics, No. 1A, Suwasala, Hanwella Road, Pugoda, Tel. 94-772133341, http://www.herbalexotic.com

Jayampathi Lanka Exports, Muttetugala, Kurune Gala, Kurunegala, Tel. 94-37-2224068, http://www.jayampathi.com

Thailand

PPK Growth Co Ltd, 1/68 1701, Bang Sri Muang, Tel. 66-897-756782, http://www.th1056386405.trustpass.alibaba.com

Eternal Herb Group, 39/231 Nawamin 143 Nuan Chan, Bueng Kum, Bangkok 10230, Tel. 668-5-0445705, http://www.eternalsoap.com

Ubon Central Shop Ltd, Kupshek, Ubon, Tel. 66-845-190319, http://www.th1073077643.fm.alibaba.com

Vietnam

Vietstar Import-Export Co. Ltd
237 Le Duc Tho Street, Ward 17, Go Vap District, Ho Chi Minh, Ho Chi Minh City 70000, Tel. 84-8-35888673, http://www.vietstar.co.on

ARABIAN PENINSULA

Dubai

The Himalaya Drug Company FZCO, Dubai Airport Free Zone Authority, Phase - 4, Block (B), 4th Floor, PO Box 54637, U.A.E., Dubai, U.A.E., Tel. 9714-204-5455, http://www.himalayaherbals.com

Oman

New Prism International LLC, PO Box -317, Muscat, Muscat, Tel. 0096892625668, Fax: 00968244799865

AUSTRALASIA

Australia

The Neem Man, Paul Thompson, 121 Cash Road, Verriedale Qld 4562, Tel. 0423077415, http://www.neemman.com

Neeming Australia Pty Ltd, 3/17 Commercial Drive, Ashmore, Queensland 4215, Tel. 07-5527-0546, Intl. 61-7-5527 0546, http://www.neemaus.com.au

Neemoil Australia Imports, PO Box 196, Croydon Park, 2133 NSW, Tel. 02-97978062 02, 96007182, http://www.neemoil.com.au

Neem Health Plus, 87 Quarry Road, Murwillumbah, NSW 2484, Tel.. 02-6672-5309, http://www.neemproductsaustralia.com,

Neem Rich Australia Unit 3/17 Commercial Drive, PO Box 95 Ashmore, Queensland, 4214,Tel. 61-7-5527-0546 http://www.neemrich.com

Rademi Enterprises P/L, 26 Glenelg Avenue, Wembley Donns WA 6019, Tel. 61-(8) 9204-1976, http://www.rademi.com

New Zealand

Green Trading, PO Box 20587, Auckland, 0641, Tel. (9) 9483876, http://www.greentrading.co.nz

Health Chemist, 47 Clyde Road, Browns Bay, Auckland 0630, Tel. 8-0800438363, 64-94785854, http://www.healthchemist.co.nz

Naturally Neem, Whatitiri Organics Ltd, Whangarei, Tel. 021-2277 000, 021-286-8600, http://www.naturallyneem.co.nz

Green Trading, PO Box 20587, Auckland, Tel. 9-9483876, http://www.greentrading.co.nz

CENTRAL AMERICA

Bahamas
Abaco Neem, 1 Don McKay Blvd., PO Box AB-203/7, Marsh Harebour, Abaco, Tel. 1-242-367-4117, http://www.abaconeem.com

Dominican Republic
Karibcial Comapny, Calle Generoso Diaz, Santiago Cibao, Turks and Cailos Island, Tel. 649-244-0887, http://www.gmdu.net/corp-54603.html

Guatemala
Ganz S.A., 1 Avda 7-57, Guatemala 9014, Tel. 502-23682669, http://www.gmdu.net/corp-774373.html

Mexico
Neem Aloe Products de Mexico SA de C.V., Calle 21 No. 202-A X 14Y 16, Col. San Miguel, Merida, Yucatan, Tel. 999-927- 0127 Y 9261670, http://www.neemaloeproducts.com

Mayan De Mexico, Mariquita Sanchez, #180 CTM Culhuacan, CP 04489, Del. Coyoacan, Tel. 552- 380-8445, 5514-388265, http://www.mayaneem.com

Laboratoria Neem-Mex, Calle De La Granja #11, Qyebrantadero Municipio Axohiapan,, C.P. 6297, Morelos, Tel. 01 (769) 17080-50 http://www.laboratorianeem-mex.com

Planters Mexico S.A., Ave. Juan Floresy Casas #906, Juchitepec 56860, Tel. 52-597-9770280, http://www.plantesmexico.com

Trinidad-Tobago
HOS Botanicals Ltd, 9F - 4th Street, Simeon Road, Petit Valley 0000, Tel. 1-868f-633-2046, http://www.hosbotanicals.com

EUROPE

Austria
Sonnentag e.u. Kerala Ayurveda Shop, Neubaugasse 62/7, 1070 Vienna, Tel. 43-1-522-5726, http://www.keralaayurvedashop.com

France
Nature Neem Products, Dr. Ashok Sundaram, M.Sc., (Agri), PhD, 57 Rue Louis Joyeux, 91100 Corbeil Essonnes, Tel. 0033-0950833121, http://www.natureneem.com

Germany
La Cara Natur, Efeuweg 3, La Care Norten, 22299 Hamburg, Tel. 49-(0)40 515932, http://www.lacara-natur.de

Terra Nostra GmbH, Alemannenstr. 5, Gewerbegeviet Ilmendorf, 85290 Geisenfeld, Tel. 49-8457-9344, 800-254-4000, http://www.terra-nostra.info

Trifolio – M, GmbH, Dr. Hans-Wilhelmi-Weg 1, 35633 Lahnau, Tel. 49 (0) 6441-209770, 63114, http://www.trifolio-m-de

Natura Medica, Friedrich-Ebert-Str. 87, 34119 Kassel, Tel. 49 (0) 561-7394000, http://www.naturamedica.de

Sat Nam Versand, Ringstr. 98, 64823 Gross-Umstadt, Tel. 49 (0) 6078-789060, http://www.satnam.eu

Kraeuterey Luetzel, Im Stillen Winkel 5, 57271 Hilcuhenbach-Luetzel, Tel. 40 (0) 2733-3846, http://www.kraeuterey.de (supplies only Neem trees as indoor plants)

Amansi Products GmgH, Am Flugplatz 9, 83126 Flintsbach, Tel. 49 (0) 8034-706566, http://www.amansi.de

Niem-Handel GmbH, Walstr. 3, 64579 Gernsheim, Tel. 49 (0) 6258-949555, http://www.niem-handel.de

Kaya Veda Ayurvedische Spezialkosmetick GmbH, Schaetzlerstr. 4, 86150 Augsburg, Tel. 49 (0) 821-567-450 0, http://www.kaya-veda.de

Ayus GmbH, Am Dreschschopf 1, 77815 Buehl-Moos, Tel. 49-(0) 7227-600990, http://www.oshadhi.eu

Dr. Scheller Cosmetics AG, Schillerstr. 21-27, 73054 Esslingen, Tel. 49 (0) 7161-8030, http://www.drpscheller-cosmetics.de

Hood Media GmbhH, Glashuettenstr. 4, 52349 Dueren, Tel. 49 (0) 2421-9947306, , http://www.hood.de

Italy

Natural Biological World, Via Bolivia 5, Paderno Dudnano 20037, Tel. 02-91082365, http://.www.natural-biological-world.com

Latvia

SIA Himalayan Drug Company, Elizabethes Street 11-10, Riga, LV-1010, Tel. 371 67854168, http://www.himalayadirect.com

Poland

Aura Globe Trade Jaroslaw Paul

23 Marca 77/3, Sopot, Tel. 48-533111343, http://www.auraglobtrade.com

Portugal

 M & M Biotechnology, Avenida eng Luis Ave Vedo Coutinho 306, 4460 - 170 Senhora da Hora, Matosinhos, Tel. 351-911-072 000, http://www.mmbiotechnology.com

Spain

Ayur Neem, Ramon Y Cajal 5, 2lzq, 28801 Calcala de Henares, Espana, Tel. +34-918-770-024, http://www.ayur-neem-com

Productos de Neem, O Tomb 9, San Salvador de Meis, Pontevedra, Tel. +34-634402095, http://www.productosdeneem.com

Biospangeo, Pisidro Ru 1219, Lorca, Mutzcia 187b, Tel. 34-968-185349, http://www.biospangea.com

Switzerland

Neem-Trade, Markus Bloesch, CH - 442 Muenchenstein, Tel. 61-821-2555, http://www.neem-trade.ch

United Kingdom

Akoma International, Unit 5 Osmaston Road, Business Park, Derby, Derbyshire, De23 8Ld, Tel. 44—01332-546930, http://www.akomaskincare.co.uk

Detox Trading, 10 Huxhams Cross, Darlington, Totnes, Devon TQ9 6Nt, Tel. 01803-762368, http://www.detoxtrading.com

EKONEEM Sales & Information, Lornty, Blairgowrie, Perthshire PH10 6TB Tel. 44- 01250-8733204, http://www.ekoneem.com

Mekuti, Glendale, Newlay Ave., Leeds, West Yorkshire, LS18 4LN, Tel. 01132-590-589, http://www.mekuti.co.uk

Neem Genie Co Ltd, online-sstore, Swan Inn, Waters Uptown, Telford, TF6 6NP, Tel. 01952-541980, http://www.neemgenie.co.uk

Serendipity Herbals Ltd, T/A The Neemteam, Unit 47 Enterprise Way, Newport, NP 20 2AQ, Tel. (0) 1633-263567, http://www.neemteam.co.uk

The House of Mistry, 15-17 Siuth End Road, Belize Park, London, NW3 2PT, Tel. 44 207794-0848, http://www.houseofmistry.com

The Neem People, Perpetua Herbals, The Barn, Denant Mill, Dreenhill Haverfordwest, Pembrokeshire, Wales, SA62 3TS, Tel. 44 (0) 1437-764415, http://www.theneempeople.com

NORTH AMERICA

Canada

Ferlow Botanicals, PO Box 30099, Marpole RPO, Vancouver, B.C., V6P 6S3, Tel. 604-322-4080, for North America toll-free 1-888-747-6287, http://www.ferlowbotanicals.com

Moor Spa Inc., 7- 13680 Bridgeport Road, Richmond, B.C., V6V 1V3, Tel. 604-279-5561, http://www.moorspa.com

Terramera Plant Science Inc., 155 – 887 Great Northern Way, Vancouver, B.C., V5T 4T5, Tel. 604-639-9600, for North America 1-800-597-9509, http://www.terramera.com

NEEM RESEARCH, PO Box 3197, Mission, B.C., V2V 4J4, Tel. 604-820-1777, http://www.neemresearch.ca – only book sales "**Neem: Nature's Healing Gift to Humanity**"

Upaya Naturals, Toronto, Ontario, **Online store**, Tel. 416-617-3096, 855-729-8341, http://www.upayanaturals.com

USA
Adytum Retreat & Spa, 186 Skyview Drive, Mossyrock, WA 98564, Tel. 360-790-2011, 360-983-8008, http://www.adytumsanctuary.com

 All About Neem, 1767 S. Patrick Drive, Suite C, Indian Harbour Beach, Fl 32937 Tel. 321-777-6715 http://www.allaboutneem.com

Auromere Ayurvedic Importers, 2621 West Highway 12, Lodi, CA 95242, Tel. 1-800-735-4691, http://www.auromere.com

Banyan Botanicals, 6705 Eaglerock Ave. NE, Albuquerque, NM 87113, Tel. 800-953-6424, http://www.banyanbotanicals.com

The Himalaya Drug Company, 1101 Gillingham Lane, Sugar Land, TX 77478, Tel. 713-863-1622, http://www.himalayausa.com

Just Neem Body Care, N. Harrison Ave., Suite 130, Cary, NC 27513, Tel. 919-414-8826, http://www.justneem.com

Neem Aura Natural, 2001 Lotus Brand Inc., PO Box 325, Twin Lakes, WI 53181, Tel. 262-889-8561, 1-800-824-6396, http://www.neemauranaturals.com

Neemking.Org, 1909 Barton Pkwy, Austin, TX 78704, Tel. 800-481-1975, http://www.neemking.org

Nico Orgo USA Inc., 3033 Hurley Way #106, Sacramento, CA. 95864-3702, Tel. 916-489-3243, http://www.neemproducts.com

Organeem LOC, 8463 Tiger Lily Drive, Sand Ramon, CA 94582, Tel. 925-964-9095, http://www.organeem.com

Organic India, US, 5311 Western Ave., Suite 110, Boulder, Co. 80301, Tel. 888-550-8332, http://www.organicindiaus.com

The Ahimsa Alternative Inc., Neem Resource, 5113 W 98th Street #16, Bloomington, MN 55437, Tel. 952-943-9449, 1-877-873-6336, http://www.neemsource.com

Thera Neem, 2498 Commerce Court, Bowling Green, FL 33873, 1-888-989-6336, http://www.theraneem.com

Jewards International Inc., 141 Campanelli Drive, Braintree, MA 02184, Tel. 617-472-9300, http://www.bulknaturaloils.com

Le Pure, 13193 Rover Glen Ct, Herdon, Virginia, Tel. 202-437-6600, http://www.gmdu.net/corop-743567.html

Bahama – Meridan Itl, 614 Shepperd Street, Durham, NC 27701, Tel. 919-321-1244, http://www.gmdu.net/corp-155092.htlm

Neem Oil, Ala Akuukuli St, Honolulu, HI 96818, Tel. 808-358-5836, http://www.gmdu.net

Mahinani's Incorporated, PO Box 538, Anahola, HI 96703, Tel. 808-631-3193, http://www.mahinanis.com

 Marble Arch Gardens Holistic Herbals, 5717 Marble Arch Way, Alexandria, VA 22315, Tel. 703-725-9272, http://www.marblearchgardens.com,   magherbs@gmail.com,

Neem Tree Farms, 602 Ronele Drive, Brandon, FL 33511, Tel. 1-877-500-6336, http://www.neemtreefarms.com

Neem 4 Life, Broadway Street, San Antonio, TX 78217, Tel. 210-277-9444, http://www.neem4life.com

Vanilla Grass Herbs, 247 Market Street, Lockport, NY 14094, Tel. 716-990-5826, http://www.vanillagrassherbs.com

The Herb Place, 207 South - 3rd Street, Clearfield, PA 16830, Tel. 814-765-5751 theherbplace@hotmail.com

Nutrimor, 5959 Gateway West, Suite 445, El Paso, TX 79925, http://www.neempowder.com

SOUTH AMERICA

Argentina

Integracion Quimica S.R.L., Calle 141, 1321 Berazategui, Buenos Aires 1884, Plant: Calle 109, No 2039, Berazategui, Buenos Aires, Tel. (5411) 4216-1575

Brazil

BR Commercial de Lorres Ltda-ME, dos Flamboyantes, CEP 60.190, Papicu – Fortaleza, Tel. (85) 265-1058, (85) 260-3670, http://www.organeem.com.br

Orquichips Ltda, 187 Rua Oswaldo Cruz, Salvador, Bahia 4194000, Tel. 55-71-33466085, **http://www.gmdu.ne**t

Peru

Agromundial SAC, Porta 454, Lima 19, Tel. 51-94-5120158, http://www.agromundial.com

Neem and Other Organizations

AFRICA

Ethiopia
Neem Foundation of Ethiopia, 20833 Addis Ababa, Tel. 251- 91-137-8403

Kenya
Kenya Neem Foundation, PO Box 55126 Post Code 00200, Igoji House Accra Road, Nairobi, Tel. 254-202210442, http://www.kenyaneem.com

Senegal
 Senegal Neem Foundation, BP 6445, Dakar-Etoile, & 340 Jones Road, Cedar Creek, TX 78612, USA, Tel. 512-321-9911, 512-294-1732, http://www.senegalneemfoundation.org

ASIA

Bangladesh
Bangladesh Neem Foundation, House NO. 412, Road No1 29, Dew Dohs, Mohakhali, Dhaka – 1206, Tel. 88029856894, http://www.neemfoundationbd.org

India

Neem Foundation, 67-A, Vithalnagar Society, Road #12, JVPD Scheme, Mumbai, 400 049, Tel. +91 22 26206367 & 26207867, http://www.neemfoundation.org

NEEM WAVE, 805-806, Orchid Tower, Lokhandwala Township, Akurli Road, Dr. Nirrmala Kotharii, Kandivali (E), Mumbai, 400 101, Tel. 91-9820608200, http://www.neemwave.com

Neem Research and Technology Development Center, Village Gondkhairy Tehsil Kalmeshwsar, Amravati Road (NH-6), District Nagpur 440 023, Tel. 91-07118-277274

EUROPE

Italy
International Neem Network FAO, Forest Resources Div., Food and Agriculture Organization of the United Nations, Viale delle Terme di, Caracalla 1-00153, Rome,Tel. 39-06 57051, media 39-06570 53625, http://www.fao.org/forestry/neem.en

UK
The Neem Tree Trust of Kathy Miller & her husband Ken, The old Stables, Avoncliff, Bradford-on-Avon, Wiltshire, BA15 2HA Tel. 44 - 01225-865789, http://www.neemtrust.org.uk

Switzerland
Neem-Trade, Markus Bloesch, CH 4142, Muenchenstein, Tel. 0041 (0) 61-8212555, http://www.neemtrade.ch

NORTH AMERICA

Canada

Ferlow Botanicals, PO Box 30099, Marpole RPO, Vancouver, B.C., V6P 6S3, Tel. 604-322-4080, for North America toll-free 1-888-747-6287, http://www.ferlowbotanicals.com

Moor Spa Inc., 7- 13680 Bridgeport Road, Richmond, B.C., V6V 1V3, Tel. 604-279-5561, http://www.moorspa.com

Terramera Plant Science Inc., 155 – 887 Great Northern Way, Vancouver, B.C., V5T 4T5, Tel. 604-639-9600, for North America 1-800-597-9509, http://www.terramera.com

NEEM RESEARCH, PO Box 3197, Mission, B.C., V2V 4J4, Tel. 604-820-1777, http://www.neemresearch.ca – only book sales "Neem: Nature's Healing Gift to Humanity"

Upaya Naturals, Toronto, Ontario, Online store, Tel. 416-617-3096, 855-729-8341, http://www.upayanaturals.com

USA

Adytum Retreat & Spa, 186 Skyview Drive, Mossyrock, WA 98564, Tel. 360-790-2011, 360-983-8008, http://www.adytumsanctuary.com

All About Neem, PO Box 553, Monticello, FL 32344, Tel. 321-777-6715, http://www.allaboutneem.com

Auromere Ayurvedic Importers, 2621 West Highway 12, Lodi, CA 95242, Tel. 1-800-735-4691, http://www.auromere.com

Banyan Botanicals, 6705 Eaglerock Ave. NE, Albuquerque, NM 87113, Tel. 800-953-6424, http://www.banyanbotanicals.com

Himalayan Wellness, 1101 Gillingham Lane, Sugar Land, TX 77478, Tel. 713-863-1622, 800-869-4640, http://www.himalayanusa.com

Just Neem Body Care, N. Harrison Ave., Suite 130, Cary, NC 27513, Tel. 919-414-8826, http://www.justneem.com

Neem Aura Natural, 2001 Lotus Brand Inc., PO Box 325, Twin Lakes, WI 53181, Tel. 262-889-8561, 1-800-824-6396, http://www.neemauranaturals.com

Neemking.Org, 1909 Barton Pkwy, Austin, TX 78704, Tel. 800-481-1975, http://www.neemking.org

Organeem LOC, 8463 Tiger Lily Drive, Sand Ramon, CA 94582, Tel. 925-964-9095, http://www.organeem.com

Organic India, US, 5311 Western Ave., Suite 110, Boulder, Co. 80301, Tel. 888-550-8332, http://www.organicindiaus.com

The Ahimsa Alternative Inc., Neem Resource, 5113 W 98th Street #16, Bloomington, MN 55437, Tel. 952-943-9449, 1-877-873-6336, http://www.neemsource.com

Thera Neem, 2498 Commerce Court, Bowling Green, FL 33873, 1-888-989-6336, http://www.theraneem.com

Jewards International Inc., 141 Campanelli Drive, Braintree, MA 02184, Tel. 617-472-9300, http://www.bulknaturaloils.com

Le Pure, 13193 Rover Glen Ct, Herdon, Virginia, Tel. 202-437-6600, http://www.gmdu.net/corop-743567.html

Bahama – Meridan Itl, 614 Shepperd Street, Durham, NC 27701, Tel. 919-321-1244, http://www.gmdu.net/corp-155092.htlm

Neem Oil, Ala Akuukuli St, Honolulu, HI 96818, Tel. 808-358-5836, http://www.gmddu.net/corp-33622.html

Mahinani's Incorporated, PO Box 538, Anahola, HI 96703, Tel. 808-631-3193, http://www.mahinanis.com

Neem Tree Farms, 602 Ronele Drive, Brandon, FL 33511, Tel. 1-877-500-6336, http://www.neemtreefarms.com

Neem 4 Life, Broadway Street, San Antonio, TX 78217, Tel. 210-277-9444, http://www.neem4life.com

Vanilla Grass Herbs, 247 Market Street, Lockport, NY 14094, Tel. 716-990-5826, http://www.vanillagrassherbs.com

The Herb Place, 207 South - 3rd Street, Clearfield, PA 16830, Tel. 814-765-5751

Marble Arch Gardens Holistic Herbals, 2800 Gallows Road, Vienna, Virginia 22031, Tel. 703-568-1272, http://www.marblearchgardens.com

Nutrimor, 5959 Gateway West, Suite 445, El Paso, TX 79925, http://www.neempowder.com

SOUTH AMERICA

Argentina

Integracion Quimica S.R.L., Calle 141, 1321 Berazategui, Buenos Aires 1884, Plant: Calle 109, No 2039, Berazategui, Buenos Aires, Tel. (5411) 4216-1575

Brazil

BR Commercial de Lorres Ltda-ME, dos Flamboyantes, CEP 60.190, Papicu – Forttaleza, Tel. (85) 265-1058, (85) 260-3670, http://www.organeem.com.br

Orquichips Ltda, 187 Rua Oswaldo Cruz, Salvador, Bahia 4194000, Tel. 55-71-33466085, http://www.gumdu.net/corp-31267.html

Unique, Av Santos Dumont 2828, Aldeota, Fortaleza, Tel. 55 (85) 3224-6659, http://www.uniqueneem.com

Peru

Agromundial SAC, Porta 454, Lima 19, Tel. 51-94-5120158, http://www.agromundial@gmail.com

Neem Research Worldwide

The following organizations, institutions, scientists, administrators and researchers have been actively involved worldwide in the research and supporting the development of the Neem tree.

Australia

Dr. Malcom Wegener, lecturer in Agri Economics School of Natural & Rural System Management, The University of Queensland, St. Lucia campus, Brisbane Qld. 4072, Tel(07) 3365-2939 (international prefix +61 7) Fax (07) 3365-9016.

Austria

Discover Neem, Birgit Bradtke, Maria Steiner Str. 28, Langkampfen, http://www.discoverneem.com

Benin

IITA – Benin
08 BP 0932 Tri Postal, Cotonou, Tel.229-64181313, http://www.iita.org

Brazil

Dr. Rudolfo Rohr, President, Consultec Commercial E Servico Techni Cos Ltda, Ave. Anchieta 173, 12A, CJ 124, PO Box 1369, `3015-100 Campina, SP, Tel. 0192 -31-1077, Fax 0192-31-1402,

IMVA International Medical Veritas Association, Arina Alvez Do Mello #177, AltiPlano Cabo Branco, Joao Pessoa, PB 58046-310, Tel. 55 83-3512-7169, http://www.imva.org

UNIQUE, Av Santos Dumont, 2828, Sala 1101, Aldeota, Fortaleza - CE 60150, Tel. 55 83-3512-7169 http://unique-management.com, http://www.primalgroup.com

Burkina Faso
West Africa Impact Center, 15 BP 104, Quagadougou 15, Tel. 226-5043 0945, Email: rsanou@echnot.org

Canada
University of British Columbia, Professor Dr. Murray B. Isman , Faculty of Land and Food, MCML 248, 2357 Main Mall, Vancouver, B.C., V6T 1Z4, Tel. 604-822-1219, http://www.landfood.ubc.ca

University of Ottawa, Biology Dept., 75 Laurier Ave. E, Ottawa, On., K1N 6N5, Tel. 61`3-562-5700, http://www.uottawa.ca

David Suzuki Foundation, 2211 West - 4th Ave., #219, Vancouver, B.C., V6K 4S2, Tel. 604-732-4228, http://www.davidsuzuki.org

NEEM RESEARCH, PO Box 3197, Mission, B.C., V2V 4J4, Tel. 604-820-1777, http://www.neemresearch.ca

China
Mr. Tan Bing, Dy. General Manager, Yunnan Guanming Neem Industrial Development Co. Ltd, Kunming National High Tech Industry Development Zone North, Yunnan, Kunming, Tel. 86-871-5706522 Fax 86-871-5706523, E-mail: tanbing@263.net

Mr. Huang Bingsheng, Dy. Governor, Yunnan Provincial Government, Wu Hua Shan, Kunming, Yunnan 650021, Tel. 86-871-3618103, Fax 86-871-3621274

Mr. Hai Bo, Director, Dy. Bio-Resources Innovative Dev. Office of the People's Govt. of Yunnan Province, WhuHuaShan, Kunming, Yunnan 650021, Tel. 86-871-3639396, Fax 86-871-36212274, http://www.ynbrd.yn.gov.cn

Mr. Yang Chonghui, Dy. Secy. General, Yunnan Provincial Committee of the Communist Party of China & Chairman of Yunnan Provincial Committee of the Chinese People's Consultive Committee,94 Southcuihu Road, Yunnan 65031, Tel. 86-871-4092066, Email: yoh@mail.yn.cninfo.net

Mr. Wang Dexiang, Dy. Director General, Forest Dept. of Yunnan Province, 120 Qingnian Road, Kunming, Yunnan 650021, Tel. 86-871-5196724 (O) 86-871-5329858 (H), Mob. 13700663380

Mr. Zhou Ya Dong, Dy. Director, HaiNan Province Forestry Bureaus, Changjiang, Hainan 572722, Tel. 08906881128 (O), 0896881188

Mr. Huang Guangdou, Prof. Dept. Plant Protection, South China Univ. Of Tropical Agric, Danzhou, Hainan 571737, Tel. 86-0898-23304896 (O), 86-0898-23300686 (H), Fax 86-0898-23300157, Email: hl_ynllcn@Sina.cn

Mr. Ma Honbing, Dy. Mngr., Dept. Admin. Yunnan Zhongke Bio-Industry Co Ltd, south A Dong, 20 Haiyuan Middle Road, High & New Te ch Industrial Development, Zone Kunming, Yunnan, Tel. 86-871-5706523, Email: gmneem@yahoo.com.cn

Mr. Wu Zhu Jui, Director, Project Management, Di. Of Products Dev. Dept. Yunnan Guanming Neem Indusrial Dev. Co. Ltd, Kunming National High Tech Industry Dev. Zone North, Kunming, Yunnan, Tel. 86-871-5706523, Email: gmneem@yahoo.com.cn

Mr. Wu Juwen, Prof. Entomol., Institute of Plant & Environ Protection, Beijing Academy of Agric & Forestry, PO Box 2449, Beijing 100089, Tel. 88435544-431, Email: JuwenWu@163.net

Mr. Yang Ligang, Vice-General Manager, Hainan Guanhua Biotech Dev. Co Ltd, Jingui Bld., 20th Floor, 18 Longkun Road, Haikon, Hainan 570125, Tel. 0898-66515088 Mob. 13005003630

Mr. Jin Min, Vice-Presidnet & Senr. Engineer, Chinese Academy of Forestry, Wan Shou Shan Beijing 100091, Tel. 010-6288960, Email: jinmin@caf.forestry.ac.cn

Mr. Li Ping, Gen. Mngr. Yunnan Guanming Neem Industrial Dev. Co Ltd, Kunming National High Tech Industry Dev. Zone North, Kunming, Yunnan, Tel. 86-871-5706622, Fax 86-871-5706523, Mob. 12888526028

Mr. Wang Quan, Chairman, Board of Directors, Yunnan Honghe Guanming Co Ltd, Yunnan Guanming Neem Industries Dev. Co Ltd, 120 Xian Road, Kaiyuan, Yunnan 661000, Mob. 013908847793, Fax 86-871-7122528

Mr. Li Shengnan, Gen. Mngr. Hainan Branch Shenzen Bio-Engineering Co Ltd, Hainan Neem Bio-Engineering Coc Lltd, R126-1208, Jinghang Tower, Airport, Haikou, Hainan, Mob. 13976089322

Mr. Chen Shougen, Chairman, Board of Supervisors, Yunnan Neem Industrial Deve. Co Ltd, Kunming National High Tech Industry Dev. North Zone, Kunming, Yunnan, Tel. 86-871-5706522, Email: gmneem@yahoo.com

Mr. Ma Xianda, Director, Neem Plantation Dev. Dept. Yunnan Guanming Neem Industrial Dev. Co Ltd, Kunming Natiional High Tech Industry Dev. North Zone, Kunming, Yunnan, Tel. 86-871-5706523, Email: gmneem@yahoo.com.cn

Mr. He Xuexiang, Insect Pathol & Biocontrol, Guangdon Forest Res. Institute, London, Guanghzou 510520

Mr. Zhang Yanping, Research Institute of Resources insects, Chinese Academy of Forestry, Yunnan 650216, Email: kczws@public.km.yn.cn, neem@km169.net

Mr. Lai Yongqi, Prof. Research Institute of Resources insect, Chinese Academy of Forestry, Want Qiao, Kunming, Yunnan 650216, Tel. 86-871-3853904, Fax 86-871-3854821, Email: kczws@public.kmyn.cn

Mr. Li Yunshou, Entomologist & Assoc. Prof. Biotech, Res. Institute, Yunnan Academy of Agric Sciences, Kunming City, Yunnan 650223, Tel. 86-871-5183204

Mr. Mao Zhendong, Director, Product Dev. Dept. Yunnan Guanming Neem Industrial Dev. Co Ltd, Kunming National High Tech Industry Dev. Zone North, Kunming, Yunnan, Tel. 86-871-5705347, Email: gmneem@yahoo.com.cn

Mr. Shi Minghui, Dy. Director Generla, Foreign Affairs Office, The People's Govt. of Yunnan Province, 230 Dacuan Road, Kunming, Yunnan, Tel. 86-871-5311550, Fax 86-871-5311987, Email: shiminghui@yfao.cn, http://www.e-yunnan.com.cn, http://www.yfao.gov.cn

South China Agricultural University, Laboratory of Insect Toxicology, Guangzhou 510 642, Tel. 86-18571714629, 86-571-88165708, http://www.study-in-china.org

Finland

Mikko Pyhala, Mariankatu 15B, 00170 Helsinki, Tel. 358-44-219-0051 (former Ambassador to Venezuela, Columbia, Caribbean, Peru and Neem enthusiast)

Germany

Max Planck-Institut fuer Biochemie, Am Lopferspitz 18, 82152 Martinsried, Tel. 49-89-8578-0, http://www.biochem.mpg.de

Bundesministerium fuer Bildung und Forschung, Heinemannstr. 2, 53175 Bonn, Tel.49- 2281-9957-0, http://www.bmbf.de

Fraunhofer Patentstelle fuer die Deutsche Forschung, Leonrodstr. 68, 80636 Muenchen, Tel. 49-89-1205-404, http://www.pst.fraunhofer.de

Universisty Hohenheim, Institut for Chemie, Schloss Hohenheim 1, 70599 Stuttgart, Tel. 49-711-4590, http://www.uni-hohenheim.de

Trifolio – M GmbH., Dr.-Hans-Wilhelm-Weg 1, 35633 Lahnau, Tel. 49-6441-209770. http://www.trifolio-m.de

Bundesinstitut fuer Verbraucherschutz und Lebensmittelsicherheit, Bundesallee 50, Gebaeude 247, 38116 Braunschweig, Tel. 40-531-21497-0, http://www.bvl.bund.de

Deutsche Gesellschaft fuer Technische Zusammenarbeit (GIZ), GmbH., Postfach 5180, 65726 Eschborn, Tel. 49-6196-79-0, und Friedrich-Ebert-Allee 40, 53113 Bonn, Tel. 49-228-44-60-0, http://www.giz.de

Johannes Gutenberg University, Institut fuer Zoologie, Fachbereich Biologie, Saarstr. 21, 55099 Mainz, Tel. 49-6131-39-0, http://www.uni-mainz.de

Institute fuer Phytopathologie und Angewandte Zoologie (IPAZ), Abteilung Entomologie, Justus-Liebig University, Heinrich-Buff-Ring 26-32, 35392 Giessen, Tel. 49-64199-37601, http://www.uni-giessen.de

Ghana

Africapractice Ghana Ltd, 2nd Floor, Davies House, House NO. F730/2, 18th Lane, Osu-Re, Accra, Tel. 233 (0) 20-222-3001, http://www.africpractice.com, locations in Kenya, Nigeria, Zanania, Sout Africa, Zimbabwe, Australia, United Kingdom

India

Central Arid Zone Research Institute, Light industrial area, Jodhpur 342 003, Tel. 91-291-2786584, http://www.cazri.res.in

Indian Agriculture Research Institute, Div. of Agricultural Chemicals, Div. Nematology, Div. of Entomology New Delhi 110 012, Tel. 91-11-25843375, http://www.iari.res.in

Tamil Nadu Agricultural University, Integrated Pest Management Centre, Pappanaicken Pudur, Madurai 625 014, Tel. 91-0452-2422684, http://www.tnau.ac.in

Society for Environmental Communications, 41 Tughlakabad Institutional area, New Delhi 110 062
Tel. 91-11-91-11-29955124, http://www.downtoearth.org

Neem Mission, C.M. Ketkar, (deceased), 471 Shanivar Peth, Pune 411 030, Maharashra, India.

Centre for Plant Protection Studies, Tamil Nadu Agricultural University, Coimbatore 641 003, Tel. 91-422-6611237, http://www.sites.tanau.ac.in

The Tawar Research Foundation, E-6-8, Neb Vallely, Neb Sarai, New Delhi 110 068, Tel. 91-011 – 2953-1039

National Institute of Malaria Research, Ch/55, Satya Marg, Chank Puri, New Delhi 110 021

The Energy and Resource Institute, Darbari Seth Block, IHC Complex, Lodhi Road, New Delhi 110 003, Tel. 91-11-2468-2100, http://www.teriin.org

Ministry of Agriculture, Government of India, Mr. Shri Shadrad Pawar, Honourable Minister of Agriculture, Krishi Bhavan, New Delhi 110 091, Tel. 91-022-2378269 and 91-011-23383370

Ministry of Chemicals & Fertilizers, Government of India, Dr. Rajendra Prasad Road, Shastri Bhavan, New Delhi 110 011

Ministry of Environment & Forest, Government of India, Mr. Parya Varan Bhavan, Cgo Complex, Lodhi Road, New Delhi 110 003, Tel. 91-22-24361669, Information and Facilitation Counter Tel. 91-11-24362064

Ministry of Small Scale Industries and Agro Rural Industries, Government of India, Mr. Jayaram Ramesh, Ministry of Micro, Small and Medium Enterprise, Udyog Bhawan, Rafi Marg, New Delhi 110 011

The National Bank for Agriculture and Rural Deveopment, Plot No. 24, "G" Block Bandra – Kurla Complex, P.B. Nol 8121, Bandra (E), Mr. Devendrkumar Desai, Chairman, Mumbai 400 051, Tel. 91-26539895/96-99

Khadi & Village Industries Commission "Granmodaya", 3, Irla Road, Vile Parle (West), Mumbai 400 056, Tel. 91-26714320-22, http://www.kvic.org

National Oil Seeds and Vegetable Oil Development Board, Ministry of Agriculture, Govt. of India, 86, Sector-18, Institutional Area, Gurgaon 122 015, Tel. 91-0124-2399258, http://www.novaboard.com

The Energy and Resource Institute, Darbari Seth Blok, IHC Complex, Lodhi Road, New Delhi 110 003, Tel. 91-11-2468-2144 & 2468, http://www.terrin.org

Envis – National Botanical Research Institute, Sikandarbagh, Rana Pratap Marg 6, Hazratganj, Lucknow 226 001, Tel. 91-522-229-7932, http://www.nbrienois.in

National Bureau of Plant Genetic Resources, Indian Council of Agrcultural Research, Ministro of Agriculture (Govt. of India, Pusa campus, New Delhi 110 012, Tel. 91-11-258 43697, http://www.nbpgr.ernet.in

Arid Forest Research Institute, Post Office Kirshi Upaz Mandi, Bsni, New Delhi Road, Jodhpur 342 005, Tel. 91-291-272-2549, http://www.afri.res.in

Institute of Forest Genetics and Free Bredding, Indian Council of Forestry, Research and Education, P.B. 1061, R.S., Puram P.O., Coimbatore 641 002, Tel. 91-422-2484100, http://www.ifgtb.icfre.gov.in

Chaudhary Charan Singh Haryana Agricultural University, Hisar 125 004, Tel. 91-1800-1803001, http://www.hau.ernet.in

Tropical Forest Research Institute, Gaur Tiraha, Madhya Pradesh, Jabalpur 482 021, Tel. 91-761-404 4004, http://www.ffri.icfre.gov.in

Indian Insitute of Technology, Hauz Khas, New Delhi 110 016, Tel. 91-11-2659 7135, http://www.iitd.ac.in

Punjab State Council for Science & Technology, M.G. Sita Complex, Sector 26, Chandigarth, Chandigarth 160 19, Tel. 91-172279-2325, http://www.pscst.gov.in

Industrial Toxicology Research Centre, PO Box NO 80, Mahatma Gandhi Marg, Lucknow, 226 001, Tel. 91-522-2627586, http://www.itrindia.org

Indian Cardamom Research Institute, Spices Board, Maladumpara, Kailasanadu, PO Id Ukki Dt, Kerala 685 553, Tel. 91-04868237206, http://www.indanspices.com

Institute of Pesticides Formulation Technology, Hsidc, Sector 20, Udyog Vihar, On NH-8 opp Ambience Mali, Gurgaon 122 016, Tel. 91-0124-2348487, http://www.ipft.gov.in

Bidhan Chandra Krishi Viswavidyalaya Bckvandbvidham Chandra Agricultural University, West Bengal Po Krishi Vishwavidyalya Haringhata,

Monhanpur, Nadia 741 252, Tel. 91-330-587-9772, http://www.bckv.edu.in

Vivekananda Institute of Biotechnology, Nimpith Sri Ramvkrishna Ashram Do, Nimpith Ashram South 24, Bengal, Parganas West, 743 338, Tel. 91-3218-226003, http://www.vibsram.web.com

Israel

Agricultural Research Organization Volcanic Center, Newe Ya'Ar Research Center, PO Box 1021, Ramat Yishay 30095, Tel. 972-3-9683226, http://www.agri.gov.il

The Volcanic Center, Dept. of Toxicology, Field Crops & Entomology, PO Box 6, Bet Dagan 50250

Kenya

Egerton University, Research and Extension Division, Njuro campus. PO Box 536, Egerton 20115, Tel. 254-051-221789112, http://www.egerton.ca/ke

International Centre of Insect Physiology and Ecology, PO Box 30772 - 00100 Nairobi, Tel.. 254 (20) 863200, http://www.icipe.org

Nicaragua

Deutsche Gesellschaft fuer Techniche Zusammenarbeit (GIZ) GmbH., Apartado Postal 489, Managua, Email: giz-nicaragua@giz.de

Nigeria

International Institute of Tropical Agriculture, PMB 5320, Oyo Road, Ibadan 200 001, Tel. 234-700800-4482, http://www.iita.org

Pakistan

University of Karachi, Dept. of Zoology, Main University Road, Karachi 75270, Tel. 92-21-99261300, http://www.uok.edu.pk

Philippines

Bondoc Development Project, PO Box 33, 4300, Lucena City

Tanzania

East Africa Impact Center, Box 15205, Arusha, Tel. 255-754-480184 and 255-684-494-187, Email:ekinsey@echonet.org

Thailand

Kaesetart University, Dept. of Entomology, 50 Ngam Wong Wan Road, Ladyaow, Chatuchak, Bangkok 10900, Tel. 66-0-2579-0113, http://www.ku.ac.th

Asia Impact Center, 270/5 Tung Hoel Road, Soi 6, PO Box 64, Chiang Mai 50000, Tel. 66-53 304028 and 66-81 9920274, http://www.echonet.org/asia-impact-center

United Kingdom

KEW Royal Botanic Gardens, Kew, Richmond, Surrey, TW9 3AB, Tel. 44-20-8332-5655, http://www.kew.org

University of Greenwich, Medway campus, Central Ave., Chatham Mertime, Chatham, Kent ME4 4TB, Tel. 44-20-8331-8000, http://www.medway.ac.uk

University of Aberdeen, Dept. of Zoology, Dept. of Agriculture and Forest, King's College, Aberdeen, AB24 3FX, Scotland, Tel. 44-1224-272000, http://www.abdn.ac.uk

Unep World Conservation Monitoring Centre, 219 Huntington Road, Cambridge, CB3 Odl, Tel. 44- (0) 1223-277314, http://www.unep-wcmc.org

United States of America
Echo Inc., 17391 Durrance Road, North Fort Myers, Fl 33917, Tel. 239-543-3246, http://www.echonet.org

University of California, Dept. Entomology, 900 University Ave., Riverside, Ca. 92521, Tel. 951-827-1012, http://www.ucr.edu

Rutgers University, 57 U.S. 1, New Brunswick, NJ 08901, Tel. 732-445-4636, http://www.rutgers.edu

School of Engineering & Applied Science, Washington University, Whitaker Hall, cmpus, Box 1097, One Brookings Drive, St. Louis, MO 63130, Tel. 314-935-7028, http://www.bmcwustl.edu

United States Department of Agriculture, Agricultural Research Service, Southern Regional Research Center, 1100 Robert E. Lee Blvd., New Orleans, LA Tel. 504-286-4214, http://www.ars.usda.gov.

Department of Entomology, University of Illinois, 320 Morrill Hall, at Urbana 4 Campaign, 505 S, Goodwin Ave., Urbana, Il 61801, Tel. 217-333-2910, http://www.life.illionois.edu

DSC The National Academies, 500 - 5th Street Nw, KWS 502, Washington, DC 20001, Tel.. 202-334-2800, http://www.sites.nationalacademies.org

Fox Chase Cancer Center, Div. Of Population Science, 7701 Burholme Ave., Philadelphia, PA 19111

Agricultural Research Service, U.S. Dept. of Agriculture, Building 007, Room 337, Barc-West, Beltsville, Maryland 20705

Organic Farming Research Foundation, PO Box 440, Santa Cruz, CA 95061, Tel. 831-426-6606, http://www.ofrf.org

Herbal & Holistic Associations, Foundations, Institutions and Societies Around the Globe

Australia

Australia Traditional Medicine Society Ltd, PO Box 1027, Suite 12, 27 Bank Street, Meadow Bank, NSW 2114, Tel. 61- (0) 2-8878-1500, http://www.atms.com.au

Complementary Medicine Association PO Box 1109, Oxenford QLD 4210 (07) 5580 5990 OR outside Australia +61 7 5580 5990 http://www.cma.asn.au

National Herbalist Association of Australia, 4 Cavendish Street, Concord West NSW 2138, Tel 61-28765 0071, http://www.nhaa.au

Canada

Academy of Classical Oriental Sciences, 303 Vernon Street, Nelson, B.C. V1L 4E3, Tel. 250-352-5887, http://www.acos.org

Alive Academy, 100 – 12751 Vulcan Way, Richmond, B.C., V6V 3C8, Tel. 60-295-9333, 1-800-663-6580, http://www.aliveacademy.com

Alternative and Integrative Medical Ssociety (AIMS), c/o University of British Columbia, 2329 W – Mall, Vancouver, B.C., V6T 1Z4, students@aims.ubc.ca, http://www.aims.ubc.ca

Ayurvedic Lifestyles Inc., 2201 Warden Ave., Suite 11, Torotno, On., M1T 1V5, http://www.ayurvedtoronto.com

Canadian College of Ayurvedic Medicine & Clinic, 166 Main Street, Toronto, On., M4E 2O8, Tel. 416-615-2839, http://www.ayurvedichealthcareclinictoronto.com

Canadian College of Holistic Health, 11160 Yonge Street, Unit 12, Richmond Hill, On. L4S 1H5, Tel. 905-884-9141, http://www.cchh.org

Centre for Ayurveda & Indian System of Healing, 305- 344 Bloor Street West, Toronto, On., M5S 3A7, Tel. 416-233-3605, http://www.caish.cag

Central College British Columbia, 55 - 8th Street, New Westminster, B.C., V3M 1N9, Tel. 604-523-2338, http://www.centralcollege.ca

College of International Holistic Studies, 1 – 9087, Derry Road, Milton, ON., L9T 7Y9, Tel. 905-864-8694, http://www.cihs.ca

College of the Rockies, 2700 College Way, Box 8500, Crankbrook, .C., V1C 5L7, Tel. 250-489-2751 1-877-489-2687, http://www.cotr.bc.ca

Dominion Herbal College, 5489 Byrne Road, Burnaby, B.C. V5J 3J1, Tel. 604-433-1926, http://www.dominionherbal.com

International Art of Living Centre, 13 Infinity Road, St-Mathieu-Du-Marc, Quebec, G0X 1NO, Tel. 819-532-3321, http://www.artofliving.ca

International College of Traditional Chinese Medicine of Vancouver, Suite 201, 1508 West Broadway, Vancouver, B.C., V6J 1W8, Tel. 604-731-2926, http://www.tcm.college.com

International Institute of Ayurveda & Complementary Medicine Inc., 1115 O'Connor Drive, Toronto, On., M4B 2T5, http://www.iiacm.com

Langara College, 100 West 49th Ave., Vancouver, B.C., V5Y 2Z6, Tel. 604-323-5322, http://www.langara.bc.ca

Oshio College of Acupuncture and Herbology, 110- 1595 McKenzie Ave., Victoria, B.C., V8N 1A4, Tel. 250-472-6601, http://www.oshiocollege.wordpress.com

Pacific Rim College, 229 – 560 Johnson Street, Victoria, B.C., V8W 3C6, Tel. 250-483-2119, http://www.pacificrimcollege.ca

PCU College of Holistic Medicine, 220- 5021 Kingsway, Burnaby, B.C., V5H 4A5, Tel. 604-433-1299, http://www.pcucollege.ca

Rhodes Wellness College, Suite 280 – 1125 Howe Street, Vancouver, B.C., V6Z 2K8, Tel. 604-708-4416, http://www.rhodescollege.ca

Wild Rose College of Natural Healing, 2435 Mansfield Drive, Unit 102, Courtenay, B.C., V9N 2M2, Tel. 250-871-8881, 888-953-7673, http://www.wrc.net

China
World Federation of Chinese Medicine Societies, No. 19.Xiaoying Road, Chaoyang District, Beijing, Tel. 86-10-58650334, http://www.wfcms.org/wfcms/englishpage/secretariat.jsp?id=419

SIBS Shanghai Institutes for Biological Sciences, CAS, 320 Yueyang Road, Shanghai 20031, Tel. 86-21-54920000, http://www.english.sibs.cas.cn/an/ct

Institute of Medicinal Plant Development, No. 151, Malianwa Road, Haidian District, Beijing 100193, Tel. 86-10-57833023, http://www.implant.ac.cn

Shanghei Traditional Chinese Medicine Research Centre, 439 Chunxiao Road, Pudong, Shanghai 201203, Tel. 86-21-50801717, http://www.sirc-tcm.sh.cn/en

United States of America
American Herbal Products Association, 8630 Fenton Street, Suite 918, Silver Spring, MD 20910, Tel. 301-588-1171

American Herbalist Guild, 125 South Lexington Ave., Susite 101, Asheville, NC 28801, Tel. 617-520-4372, http://www.americanherbalistguild.com

The Cornucopia Institute, PO Box 126, Cornucopia, Wisconsin 54827, Tel. 608-625-2000, http://www.cornucopia.org

American Holistic Health Association, PO Box 17400, Anaheim, CA 92817 – 7400, Tel. 714-779-6152, http://www.ahha.or

Association of Ayurvedic Professionals of North America, 567 Thomas Street, Suite 400, Coopersburg, PA 18036, Tel. 484-550-8036, http://www.aapma.org

International Herb Association, PO Box 5667, Jacksonville, FL 32247-5667, Tel. 904-399-3241, http://www.iherb.org

National Association for Holistic Aromatherapy, PO Box 27871, Raleigh, NC 27611-7871, Tel. 919-894-0298, http://www.naturalhealthweb.co

Mount Madonna Institute, 445 Summi Road, Watsonville, CA 95076, Tel. 408-846-4060

National Ayurvedic Medical Association, 8605 Santa Monica Blvd., Los Angeles, CA., 90069-4109, Tel. 1-800-660-8914, http://www.ayurvedanamag.org

San Diego College of Ayurveda, 725 N Quince Street, Escondito, CA 92025, Tel. 760-690-3802, http://www.sandiegocollegeofayurveda.com

The Herb Growing & Marketing Network, Maureen Rogers, Director, PO Box 245, Silver Spring, PA 17575-0245, Tel. 717-393-3295, http://www.herbnet.com/associations_p1.htm (on that website you will find most herb and herbal companies listed in North America)

United Natural Product Alliance, 1075 E Hollywood Ave., Salt Lake City, UT 84105-3446, Tel. 801-474-2572, http://www.unpa.com

United Plant Savers, PO Box 400, East Barre, VT 05649, Tel. 802-476-6457, http://www.unitedplantsavers.org

United Kingdom
British Herb Trade Association, 133 Eastgate, Louth, Lincolnshire, LN11 OWB, Tel. 44-01507-353785, http://www.bhta.org.uk

European Herbal & Traditional Medicine Practitioners Association, 25 Lincoln Close, Tewkesbury Glos GL20 5TY, Tel. 44 (0) 1684-291605, http://www.ehtpa.eu

The National Institute of Medical Herbalists Ltd, Clover House, South Street, Exeter, EX1 1EE, Tel. 44-1392-426022, http://www.nim.org.uk

Naturopathic and Botanical Organizations

ASIA

India

CSIR – National Botanical Research Institute, PO Box 436, Rana Pratap Marg, Lucknow 226 001, Tel. +91-522-2205848, http://www.nbri.res.in

International Institute of Herbal Medicine, 2/301, Vijay khand – II Gomti Nagar, Lucknow 226 010, Tel. +91 – 0522-2395552, http://www.ishm.co.in

National Institute of Ayurveda, Jorawar Singh Gate, Amer Raod, Jaipur 302002, Tel. 91-2635740, http://www.nia.nic.in

EUROPE

Belgium

Association of European Self Medication Industry, 7 Avenue de Tervuren, B-1040 Brussels, Tel. 32-2-7355130, http://www.aesgp.eu

European Federation for Complementary and Alternative Medicine, c/o EPHA, 49-51 Rue de Treves, 1040 Brussels, Tel. 0046-18301862, http://www.efcam.eu

European Federation of Associations of Health Products Manufactures, Rue Jacques de Lalaing 4, 1040 Brussels, Tel. -32-2721-64495, http://www.ehpm.org

United Kingdom

British Herbal Medicine Association, PO Box 583,The Secretary, Surrey, EX1 9GX, Tel. 44 (0) 845-680-1134, http://www.bhma.info

National Institute of Medial Herbalists, Elm House, 45 Mart Arches Street, Exeter, Devon EX4 3BA, Tel. 44 (0)1392-426022, http://www.gcwhite.o.uk

NORTH AMERICA

Canada

British Columbia

British Columbia Naturopathic Association, 2238 Pine Street, Vancouver, B.C, V6J 5G4, Tel. 604-736-6646, 800-277-1128, http://www.bcna.ca

Boucher Institute of Naturopathic Medicine, Suite 300, 435 Columbia Street, New Westminster, B.C., V3L 5N8, Tel. 604-777-9981, http://www.binm.org

Canadian Herbalist's Association of B.C., Box 8326, Victoria, B.C., V8W 3R9, http://www.chaofbc.ca

Manitoba

Herb Society of Manitoba, PO Box 61004, RPO Grant Park, Winnipeg, MB R3M 3X8, http://www.herbsocietymb.com

Nova Scotia

Herbalist Association of Nova Scotia, 989 Young Ave, Halifax, NS, B3N 2V9, http://www.herbalns.org

Ontario

Canadian Association of Naturopathic Doctors, 20 Holly Street, Ste. 200, Toronto, Ontario M4S 3B1, Tel. 416-496-8633, 1-800-551-4381, http://www.cand.ca (their members are 10 Provincial Associations and 1 from the Yukon Territory)

Canadian College of Naturopathic Medicine, 1255 Sheppard Ave East, North York, On., M2K 1E2, Tel.416-498-1255, http://www.ccnm.edu, http://www.rsnc.ca

The Ontario Herbalist Association, PO Box 123 Station D., Etobicoke, ON., M9A 4X2, Tel. 416-236-0090, http://www.herbalists.on.ca

Quebec

Canadian Council of Herbalist's Associations (CCHA), 362 Ste-Catherine, Longueil, QC, J4H 2C1 http://www.herbalccha.org

Guilde Des Herboriste, CP 475555 Plateau Mont-Royal, Montreal, QC, H2H 2S8, Tel. 514-990-7168, http://www.guildedesherboristes.org

United States of America

Bastyr University – W ashgington Campus, 14500 Juanita Drive NE, Kenmore, WA 98028-4966, Tel. 425-823-1300, http://www.bastyr.edu

Bastyr University – California Campus, 4106 Sorrento Valley Blvd, San Diego, CA, 92121, Tel. 425-823-1300, http://bastyr.edu

Natural Ayurvedic Medical Association, 8605 Santa Monica Blvd, #46781, Los Angeles, CA 90069-4109, Tel. 800-660-8914, http://www.ayurvedanama.org

Herb Research Foundation, 4140 - 15th Street, Boulder, CO 80304, http://www.herbs.org

Horst Rechelbacher Foundation, 800 TCF Tower, 121 South Eight Street, Minneapolis, MN 55402, Tel. 612-376-4500

National University of Natural Medicine, 049 SW Porter Street, Portland, OR 97201, Tel. 503-552-1555, http://www.nunm.edu

National University of Health Sciences, 200 East Roosevelt Road, Lombard, IL 60148, Tel. 800-826-6285, http://www.nuhs.edu

Southwest College of Naturopathic Medicine, 2140 East Broadway Road, Tempe, AZ 85282, Tel. 480-858-9100, http://www.scnm.edu

University of Bridgeport College of Naturopathic Medicine, 60 Lafayette Street, Bridgeport, CT 06604, Tel. 800-392-3582, http://www.bridgeport.edu

American Association of Naturopathic Physcians, 150 South Highway 160, Ste. 8-528, Pahrump, Nevada, NV 89048, Tel. 888-212-4440, http://www.anma.org

American Naturopathic Association, PO Box 3599, Ann Arbor, MN, 48103, Tel. 734-223-6720, http://www.americannaturopathicassociation.com

The American Association of Naturopathic Physicians, 4435 Wisconsin Ave., Suite 403, Washington, DC 20016, Tel. 202-237-8150, 866-438-2267, http://www.naturopathic.org

Psoriasis Support Organizations

AFRICA

Kenya
Africa Psoriasis Organization, PO Box 20548 – 00100, Nairobi, Kenya, http://www.psoriasisafrica.org

South Africa
South African Psoriasis Association, PO Box 276, Rondebosch 7701, Tel. +27 (0) 86 671 5009, http://www.psoriasis.org.za

ASIA

India
Indian Psoriasis Foundation, c/o Dr. Ambalkar's Ayurvedic Reseach Centre Pvt Ltd,ARC Bhavan, Evershine City, Mumbai, India Tel. +91 (250)24 64766

Philippines

Psorasia, Secretariat, PO Box 3196, Makati Citu Post Office, Makati City, Philippines, Tel. +632-3794290, http://www.psorasia.org/dir.html

EUROPE

France

France Psoriasis, 53 Rue Compans, 75019 Paris, +33-1 42 39 0255, France, http:// www.francesporiasis.org

UK

The Psoriasis Association, Dick Coles House, 2 Queensbridge, Northampton, NN4 7BF, United Kingdom, Tel. 08456-760076, http://www.psoriasis-association.org.uk

Sweden

International Federation of Psoriasis Association, IFPA Secretariat, Bellmansgatan 30, SE-11647 Stockholm, Sweden, Tel. +46-8-55610918, **http://www.ifpa-org** (there are 51 Psoriasis organizations worldwide listed on their website for more information).

NORTH AMERICA

Canada

Canadian Association of Psoriasis Patients, 136 – 2446 Bank Street, Suite 383, Ottawa, On., K1A 1V8, Canada, Tel. 613-294-1525, http://www.canadiansporiasis.ca

USA

National Psoriasis Foundation, 6600 SW 92nd Ave., Suite 300, Portland,. OR 97223, Tel. 503-244-7404, http://www.psoriasis.org,

International Psoriasis Council, 1034 S. Brentwood Blvd., Suite 600, St. Louis, MO 63117, Tel. 972-861-0503, http://www.psoriaiscouncil.org

SOUTH AMERICA

Argentina
Sociedad Latino Americana De Psoriasis, Avda Callao 157 PISO 9 DTO, "C", Caba, Argentina, Tel. +54- 11-4372-2388, http://www.solapso.org

Health Freedom Organizations

Canada
Association Canadienne Des Produits Naturel, 130 Place de Naples, Laval, QC, H7M 4A1, Tel. 450-967-2276, http://ww.cnpa-acpn.ca

Health Action Network Society, 214 – 5589 Byrne Road, Burnaby, B.C., V5J 3J1, Tel. 604-435-0512, 855-787-1891, http://www.hans.org

Citizens for Health Choice in Health Care Association, #343, 9768 – 170 Street, AB, T5T 5L4, Tel. 780-471-5104, http://www.citizensforchoice.com

Catherine Publishing/Let's Get Real, PO Box 478, Blackie, AB, T0L 0J0, http://www.igrcc.com, http://www.letgetrealchattincatherine.com

Natural Health Products Protection Association, 5070 Fountain Street N, Breslau, Ontario, N0B 1M0, Tel. 519-648-2050, http://www.nhppa.org, http://www.charterofhealthfreedom.org

Natural Health Freedom Canada, Ravine Park Plaza, 265 Port Union Road, Scarborough, Ontario, M1C 4Z7, http://www.naturalhealthfreedom.com

Chile
Salud Natural A.G./Vitamigos S.A., Avenida Libertador Bernardo, o'Higgins 494, Santiago, Tel. 56-2-632-1887

Denmark
May Day, Hydevadvej 12, Honkys, 6230 Rodekro, Tel. 7020-7770, http://www.mayday-info.dk

Germany
Dr. Rath Foundation, Bahnhofstr. 1/1a, 1255 Berlin, Tel. 49 (0) 30246479, http://www.4.dr-rath-foundation.org

Italy
La Leva for Freedom of Choices, La Leva Di Archimede, Rampa Brancaleone 58, 00165 Rome, Tel. 39-06635884, http://www.laleva.org

Netherlands
Dr. Rath Foundation, Sourethweg 9, 6422 Heerlen, Tel. 31-457-111-223, http://www.4.dr-rath-foundation.org

New Zealand
NZ Health Trust, Box 34-057, Christchurch, 8540, Tel. 64-335-19807, http://www.nzhealthtrust.co.nz

Natural Health Alliance, PO Box 302477, North Harbour, North Shore City 0751, http://www.naturalhealthalliance.co..nz

New Health New Zealand, Box 34-057, Christchurch 8030, Tel. 64-335—19807, http://www.newhealth.co.nz

South Africa

Traditional Natural Health Alliance, Postnet Suite 141 Private Bagxi, Vlaeberg 8018, Tel. 27-723777-598, http://www.naturalhealthalliance.co.za

Sweden

National Health Federation c/o Sara Boo, Vitsippan A7, 26531 Astorp, http://www.thenhf.se

United Kingdom

Alliance for Natural Health, The Artrium, Curtis Road, Dorking, Surrey, RH4 XA, Tel. 44 (0) 1306-646600, http://www.anh-europe.org, http://www.anhinternational.org

Consumers for Health Choice, Southbank House, Black Prince Road, London, SE1 7SI, Tel. 44-020-7463-0690, http://www.consumersforhealthchoice.com

National Health Federation, c/o Emma Currie, Acting Up Belgrave Business Centre, 45 Frederick Street, Edinburgh, EH2 1EP,http://www.thenhf.co.uk

USA

National Health Federation, PO Box 688, Monrovia, CA 91017, Tel. 626-357-2181, http://www.thenhf.com

Dr. Rath Foundation, PO Box 4103, Santa Clara, CA 95056-4103, Tel. 800-648-7171, http://www.4.dr-rath-foundation.org

National Health Freedom Coalition, PMB 218, 2136 Ford Parkway, St. Paul, MN 55116-1863, Tel. 651-690-0732, http://www.nationalhealthfreedom.org

Alliance for Natural Health, Piedmont Center, Building 5, 3525 Piedmont Road NE, Suite 110, Atlanta, GA 30305, Tel. 800-230-2762, http://www.anh-usa.org

The Health Keeper Alliance, 220 Parker Street, Warsaw, IN 46580, Tel. 888-965-5005, http://www.healthkeepers.net

Sunshine Health Freedom Foundation, 5317 Bluebonnet, Colleyville, TX 76034, http://www.sunshinehealthfreedom.org

Citizens Council for Health Freedom, 161 St Anthony Ave., Ste 923, St Paul, MN 55703, Tel. 651-646-8935, http://www.cchfreedom.org

California Citizens for Health Freedom, 1511 Robinson Street No. 303, Oroville, CA 95965, http://www.citizenshealth.org

International Advocates for Health Freedom, 556 Boundary Bay Road, Point Roberts, WA 98281, Tel. 800-333-2553, Tel. 360-945-0352, http://www.nocodexgenocide.com

References

Ad Hoc panel of the Board on Science and Technology for International Development, National Research Council. (1992) *Neem: A Tree for Solving Global Problems.* Washington, D.C., National Academy Press.

Agrawal D.P. (undated) *Medicinal properties of Neem: New Findings*, http://www.infinityfoundation.com/mandala/t_es/t_agraw_neem.htm)

American Journal of Therapeutics (2007) *Fractionated Neem leaf extract is safe and increases CD4+ cell levels in HIV/AIDS patients.* Jul-Aug; 14(4):369-74.

Bandyopdhyay U, Biswas K., Sengupta A, et al. (2004) *Clinical studies on the effect of Neem (Azadirachta indica) bark extract on gastric secretion and gastroduodenal ulcer.* Life Science 75:2867-78.

Bhandri, .P.R., Mukerji B.(1987) *The Neem: Indian lilac (Azadirachta indica)* The Eastern Pharmacist, Jan.:2(13):21-24.

Bhargava .K.P. (1987) *Neem oil as a synergist to anti-diabetic drugs for management of secondary hyperglycemia.* Neem Newsletter, 4(3):31-32.

Bhatnagar .D, Zeringue H.J., (1993) *Neem Leaf extract (Azadirachta indica) inhibit biosynthesis in aspergillus flavus and A. Parasiticus.* Proceedings of the World Neem Conference, Bangalore, India Feb. 24 – 28.

Caius JF, Mhaskar KS. (undated)*The correlation between the chemical composition of anthelminthic and their therapeutic values in connection with the hookworm inquiry in the Madras Presidency.* Indian J. Med Res, 123:11:353-70

Charles .V, Charles S.X. (1992) *The use and efficacy of Azadirachta indica (neem) and Curcuma longa (turmeric) in scabies. A pilot study.* Tropical Medicine. 44(102):178-81.

Chinnassmy. N. Et.al. (1993) *Toxicological studies on debitterized neem oil.* Food Chem. Toxicol, Apr; 31(4)297-301.

Chopra I.C., Gupta K.C. and Nazir B.N. (1952) *Preliminary study of antibacterial substances form Melia azadirachta.* Indian Journal of Medical Research 40: 511-515.

Dakhinmurthi. K.(1954) *The amino acids in the leaf of Azadirchata indica (Melia).* Current Science (Bangalore), 23: 125-126.

Ekanem, O.J. (1978) *Has Azadirachta indica (Dongoyaro) any anti-malaria activity?* Nigerian Medical Journal. 8: 8-10.

Fujiwara .T, Takeda T, Ogihara Y., Shimizu T, Tomita Y., Sugishita E, Nomura T. (1984) *Further studies on the structure of polysaccharides from the bark of the Melia azadirachta.* Chemical and Pharmaceutical Bulletin 32: 1385 – 1391.

Gandhi. M. Lal, R. Sankaranarayanan, A. Banerjee. C.K. Sharma. P.L. (1988) *Acute toxicity study of the oil from Azadirachta indica (neem oil).* Journal of Ethnopharmacology. 23: 39-51.

Garg. H.S., Bhakumi, D.S. (1984) *An isoprenylated flavanone form leaves of Azadirachta indica.* Phytochemistry, 23: 2115-2118.

Garg. G.P. Nigam. S.K. Ogle. C.W. (1993) *The gastric antiulcer effects of the leaves of the neem tree.* Planta Medica (59) 215 – 217.

Garg S., Taluja V., Upadhyay SN, Talwar GP, (1993) *Studies on the contraceptive efficacy of Praneem polyherbal cream.* Contraception 48:591-6.

Grant, I.F., Seegers. K., Walanabe. I. (1984) *Increasing biological nitrogen fixation in flooded rice using neem.* In Proceedings of the 2nd International Neem Conference, Ravischholzhausen, West Germany May 25, 1983 pp. 493 – 506.

Iwu. M.M., Obidoa. O., Anazzodo. M. (1986) *Biochemical mechanism of antimalaria activity of Azadirachta indica leaf extract.* Pharmacological Research Communications. 18: 81 – 91.

Khan. M, Wassilew. S.W. (1987) *The effects of raw material from the neem tree, neem oil and neem extracts on fungi pathogenic to humans.* In Proceedings of the 3rd International Neem Conference, Nairobi, Kenya, July 10, 1986 pp. 685-650.

Koul. O.B., Kethkar. C.M., (1990) *Properties and uses of neem.* Can. J. Bot. 68:1 – 11.

Lorenz. H.K.P., (1976) *Neem tree bark extract in the treatment of inflammatory stomatitis.* Zahanaerztl. Praxis 8: 1 – 4.

Mishra AK, Singh N, Sharma VP. (1995) *Use of neem oil as a mosquito repellent in tribal villages of Mandia district, Madhya Pradesh.* Indian J Malariol 32:99-103.

Mukherjee. S, Lohiya. N.K., Pal. R., Sharma. M.G., Talwar. G.P., (1996) *Purified neem Azadirachta indica seed extracts (Praneem) abrogate pregnancy in primates.* Contraception. Jun: 53(6): 375-8.

Nwafor SV, Akah PA, Okli CO, et al (undated) *Interaction between chloroquine sulphate and aqueous extract of Azadirachta indica A. Juss (Meliaceae) in rabbits.* Act Pharm 2003:53:305=11.

Okpako. D.T., (1977) *Prostaglandin synthetase inhibitory effect of Azadirachta indica.* Journal of West African Science Association. 22: 45 – 47.

Pai MR, Acharya LD, Udupa N. (1992) *The effect of two different dental gels and a mouthwash on plaque and gingival scores. A pilot study.* Trop Georgor Med 44:178-81.

Pai MR, Acharya LD, Udupa N. (2004) *Evaluation of antiplaque activity of Azadirachta indica leaf extract gel – a 6 week clinical study.* J. Ethnopharmacol 9-:99-103.

Pillai. N.R., Suganthan. D., Seshadri. C., Santhakumari. G., (1978) *Analgesic and anti-pyretic actions of nimbidin.* Bull. Med. Ethno. Bot, Res. 1: 393 – 400.

Pillai. N.R., Santhakumri. G., (1981) *Anti-arthritic and anti-inflammatory actions of nimbidin.* Planta Medica 43: 59 – 63.

Porter Anna Horsbrugh, (17 April 2006), *Neem: India's tree of life* (http://www.news.bbc.co.uk /2/hi/south_asia/4916044.stm). BBC News.

Rahman S.Zillur and Jairajpuri M. Shamin. (1996) *Neem in Unani Medicine,* Neem Research and Development Society of Pesticide Science, New Delhi,

India, 1993, p. 208-219 Eds. N.S. Randhawa and B.S. Parmar, end revised edition (chapter 21).

Rembold H. (1989) The *azadirachtins – their potential for insect control.* EconMedPlant Res 3:57-72.

Sawanobori. H. (1978) *Melia azadirachta (neem) extract for skin cosmetics.* Chem. Abstr., 88:11747s.

Schmutterer H, Ascher KRS, Isman MB, et al eds. (1995) *The Neem Tree: Azadirachta indica A. Juss and Other Meliaceous Plants,* Weinheim, Germany:

Schmutterer H, (2002) *The Neem Tree, Azadirachta indica A. Juss, and other meliaceous plants, sources of unique natural products for integrated pest management, medicine, industry and other purposes,* 2nd edition, Neem Foundation, Bombay, India.

Schumacher, M., Cerella, C., Reuter, S., Dicato, M., & Diederich, M. (2011). *Anti-inflammatory, pro-apoptotic, and anti-proliferative effects of a methanolic neem (Azadirachta indica) leaf extract are mediated via modulation of the nuclear factor-κ B pathway.* Genes & Nutrition, 6(2), 149–160. doi:10.1007/s12263-010-0194-6

Singh. N, Sastry. M.S. (1981) *Anti-microbial activity of neem oil.* Indian Journal of Pharmacology. 13: 102.

Thompson. E.B., Anderson. C.C. (1978) *Cardiovascular effects of Azadirachta indica extract.* J. Of Pharmacological Science 67: 1476- 1478.

Transactions of the Royal Society of tropical medicine and hygiene (2006) *A polyherbal vaginal pessary with spermicidal and antimicrobial action: evaluation of its safety.* Dec;100.

Bibliography

Abraham Sara (2014) *Neem: The tree of Life*. Ryder Management Inc.

Ajesh Kumar, Meena H.S. (2013) *Comparative Utilization of Neem green leaves*, Lap Lambert Academy Publishing.

Arif Sana, Zia ur Rahmn, Abbas Naheed (2012) *Effect on Neem based mosquito repellent*. Lap Lambert Academy Publishing.

Arunima Sarna, Bhattachryya Krishnag. (2013) *Biosorbent form Neem leaves*, Lap Lambert Academy Publishing.

Baranay Inez (2006) *Neem Dreams*, Amazon Digital Services.

Chaturvedi Suresh (1998) *Neem in Ayurveda*, Bhavan's Book University.

Conrick John. (2001) *Neem – The Ultimate Herb*, Neem Association.

Dipannitat Datta (2005) *A bouquet of short stories*. Banaphool, Rupa.

Grover Sukhmani. (2014) *Neem and its miraculous healing powers*, Amazon Digital Services.

Hassanein Naziha (2013) *Antimicrobial Benefits of Neem tree*. Lap Lambert Academic Publishing

Hakim M.A. (2015) *Neem: Cultivation, processing and uses, Bangladesh* Neem Foundation.

Haupka Katrin, (2009) *Neem: Inhaltsstoffe im organischen Landbau,* Grin-Verlag.

Henne, Sherrie K. (2011) *Neem: A hands-on guide to one of the world's most versatile herbs.* Scribd.

Icon Group International (2010) *Neem: Websters Timeline History 1857 – 2007.* Icon International Group.

Jarrad, GM. (2006) *Neem: Health benefits from India's tree of life,* Woodland Publishing.

Johri Tulika (2013) *Neem Oil, A remedy to the hazardous effects of cypermethrin.* Lap Lambert Academic Publishing.

Kabra Kamal Nayan, Upadhyay (undated) *Development and Ecological Role of Neem in India,* Institute of Public Administration for Neem Foundation, Mumbai

Kavathekar Ky (2003*)   Neem in India, The Publications & Information Directorate,* CSIR.

Kim Marian (2014) *Neem.* Amazon Digital Services.

Kluge Heidelore (1996) *Die Kraft der indischen Wunderpflanze,* Ludwig-Verlag.

Koul Opender, Wahap Seena (2011) *Neem: Today and in the new millennium,* Kluwer Academic Publisher.

Matthew Susan, Chawala S.L., Dhaduk BK. (2012) *Effect of foliar vesus Neem oil coated urea on Turfgrass.* Lap Lambert Academy Publishing.

Narval S.S. (2003) *Neem: In sustainable Agriculture*, Scientific Publishing Journal.

National Academy Press. (1992) *Neem – A Tree for Solving Global Problems.*

Norten Ellen.(2000) *Neem: India's Miraculous Healing Plant*, Healing Arts Press.

Neem Foundation, (1996) *Neem: Application in Agriculture, Health Care and Environment*, Neem Foundation.

NII Board of Consultants & Engineers, (undated) *Hand Book on Neem and Allied Products*, Asia Pacific Press Inc

Otieno Onesimus. (2009) *Toxicology effects of Neem on the squash bug*, VDM-Verlag.

Paterson Pamela. (2012) *Neem: Benefits for health and the environment*, CreativeSpace Independent Publishers.

Paterson Pamela, Robert Long. (2012) *Health benefits of Neem from the Abaco Neem Farm*, Pamela Paterson.

Prakash Srivastra Ram. (2002) *Neem and Pest Management*, International Book Distributors.

Puri H.S., Puri Puri. (1999) *Neem: The divine tree – Azadirachta indica*, Harwood Academic Publishers.

Randhawa N.S., Parmar B.C. (2007) *Neem*, New Age International.

Russel, Jes, Cohn Ronald. (2012) *Neem Cake*, Bookvika Publishing.

Schmutterer, Prof. Dr. Heinrich. (2002) *The Neem Tree*, 2nd edition, Neem Foundation, Bombay, India.

Shanaz Hanif, Khajista Jabeen, Shagupta Naz (2013) *Antifungal potential of Neem extract against alternaria solani*, Lap Lambert Academy Publishers.

Singh Dueep Jyot (2015) *The Healing power of Neem - Margosa - time tested remedies for common ailments*, JD-B12 Publishing

Singh Dueep, Davidson John (2014) *The Magic of Neem Margosa to Heal*, JD-Biz Corp Publishing.

Singh D.K. (2003) *Neem in Human and Animal Health*, IBDC Publishers.

Singh K.K., Phogat Suman, Dhillon, R.S., Tomar Ala, (2009) *Neem: A Treatise*, IK International Publishing.

Singh Neeraj Pratap. (2009) *Neem – The Village Pharmacy*, Singh International Book Distribution Co.

Sunder Shyam. (2006) *Neem: For organic farming and health*, JV Publishing.

Tewari D.N. (1992) *Monograph on Neem – Azadirachta indica A. Juss* , International Book Distributor.

Vaishnava C.S., Kumar Ajesh, Meena H.S. (2013) *Comparative Utilization of Neem*. Lap Lambert Academic Publishing

Verma G.S. (2010) *Miracles of the Neem Tree*. Sarawati Library.

Verma Vijay Chandra (2012) *Microbial Endophytes of Neem*, Lap Lambert Academic Publishing.

Vijaalakshmi K. (1995) *Neem: A user manual*, Centre of Indian Knowledge System & Research Foundation.

Witte Frank, Bungert Bernd, Frerich Thomas (2011) *Sustainable Neem oil usage in Ghana, Nachhaltige Nutzung von Neem* Oil. Shaker Verlag GmbH.

Ayurveda & Environment

Allen Joseph. (2005)   *Ancient medicine of globalization*, University of Pennsylvania Press.

Alvres Claude (2011) *The Organic Farming, Source Book*. India Press.

Baharu Islam K.M. (2001*) Defending Traditional knowledge rights, India's legal battle against turmeric, basmati rice and Neem patents in USA and Europe*. VDM Verlag.

Caldecott, Ted. (2006) *Ayurveda – The divine of Life*, Mosby Elsevier.

Frawley David, Vasant Lad (1992) *The Yoga of Herbs, A Ayurvedic Guide to Herbal Medicine*, Lotus Press.

Frawley David, (2001) *Ayurvedic Healing*, Lotus Press.

Green Jed, Kenny Bruno (1997) *Greenwash: The reality behind corporate environmentalism.* TWN.

Joshi Abhay (2012) *Organic farming and marketing in India.* Lap Lambert Academy Publishing.

Kampmann Klaus, Staehelin Thomas (2013) *Striving towards personal health and happiness.* Flow Zone Edition.

Kutumbia P. (1999). *Ancient Indian medicine*, Orient Longman.

Miller Light, Miller Bryan. (1996) *Ayurveda & Aromatherapy, The Earth essential guide to ancient wisdom*, Lotus Press.

Pole Sebastian. (2006) *Ayurvedic Medicine*, Churchill Livingstone Elsevier.

Schmutterer Heinrich, Hueber Joerg (2005) *Natuerliche Schaedlingsbekaempfungsmittel.* Ulmer Verlag.

Schmutterer Heinrich (2009) *Tropische Insekten – Meisterwerke der Evolution.* Westarp Wissenschaften

Shiva, Vandana (2013) *Making peace with the Earth: Beyond resource, land and food wars.* Pluto Press.

Shiva, Vandana, Shreya Jani Sulakshana M. Fontana (2011) *The Great Indian Land Grab*, Navdanya.

Shiva, Vandana, Barker Debbie, Lockhart Caroline (2011) *The GMO Emperor has no cloth*, Navdanya.

Shiva, Vanada, Kuma Bhatt Vinod. (2009) *Climate Change at the third pole.* Navdanya.

Shiva, Vandana (1997) *Biopiracy: The plunder of nature and knowledge.* South End Press.

Shiva, Vandana (1991) *The violence of green revolution.* Zed Books & TWN.

Sidhu Balvinder, (2011). *Das Ayurveda Gluecksbuch, Herzensziel in 6 Stufen*, Suedwest-Verlag.

Sidhu Balvinder. (2008) Haarausfall – *Ayurvedische Ansichten und Loesungsansaetze*, Erd-Verlag.

Vasand Lad. (2004) *Ayurveda: The science of self-healing*, Lotus Press.

Wuyastyk Dagmar, Smith Frederich. (2000) *Modern and global Ayurveda*, State University of New York.

Zueniga Maria Hamlin, Peralta Arturo Quizhpe (2007) *Voices of the Earth: from Savor to Cuenca.* TWN, PHM, People Health Assembly.

Recommended Reading

Health, Healing and Herbs

Applequist W (2006) *The identification of medical plants handbook of the morphology of botanicals in commerce.* American Botanical Council.

Baker Catriona (2014) *The Man of the Trees.* South Canterbury Museum.

Balch Phillis (2000) *A Prescription for Herbal Healing.* Penguin.

Blech Joerg (2007*) Herzlose Medizin, Fragwuerdige Therapien und wie Sie sich davor schuetzen koennen,* Fischer Taschenbuch Vlg.

Blech Joerg, Tuffs, A. (2003). *Die Krankheitserfinder: Wie wir zu Patienten gemacht werden* [Disease Mongers: How we all become Patients]. *BMJ : British Medical Journal, 327*(7424).

Bratman S, Kroll D, (1999) *Natural Health Bible.* Prima Publishing.

Braun M, Vanderhaeghe L (2014) *Beautiful Skin begins within.* Friesens.

Brownstein Art (2005) *Extraordinary Healing, the amazing power of your body's healing secret,* Harbor Press.

Buhner Stephen Harrod (2012) *Herbal Antibiotics: Natural alternatives for treating drug-resisted bacteria*. Storey Publishing.

Clement Anna Maria (2007) *A Family Guide to health and healing*. Waterside.

Clevely Andi (2001) *Richmond Katherine, The Complete book of herbs*. Hermes House.

Carolyn Dean (2006)*The magnesium miracle*. Ballantine Books.

Davis Wade, Weil Andrew (2004)*The Lost Amazon: the photographic journey of Richard Evans Schultes*. Thames & Hudson Ltd.

Davis Wade (2009)*The Wayfinders: Why ancient wisdom matters in the modern world*. House of Anansi Press.

DeMaco Carolyn (2000) *Doctor DeMarco answers your questions – Natural remedies for common health problems*. Well Women Press.

Duke James (2000) *The Green Pharmacy Herbal Handbook*. Rodale Press Inc.

Evans Schultes Richard (1990) *Healing Forest: Medicinal and toxic plants of the North West*. Timber Press.

Eldin Sue, Dunford Andrew (1999) *Herbal Medicine in primary care*. Butterworth-Heinemann.

Gerard John (1975) *The Herbal or General History of Plants*. Dover Publications.

Gifford-Jones (2013) *What I learned as a medical journalist, a collection of columns.* Friesen Corp.

Gladstar Rosemary (1993) *Herbal healing for women.* Touchstone.

Gurudas (2014) *The spiritual properties of herbs.* DP Inc.

Hawkey Sue (1997) *Herbalism – for health and well-being.* Anne Publishing Ltd.

Hoffmann, David (2003) *Medical Herbalism, the science and practice of herbal medicine*, Healing Arts Press.

Holzer Hans (1994) *Healing beyond medicine*, Longmeadow Press.

Hutchens, Alma R, Tretchikoff N.G. & Natalie (1969) *Indian Herbology of North America*, Merco.

Jensen Bernard (1992) *Herbs: Wonder Healer.* Bernard Jensen International.

Jensen Bernard (1978) *Nature has a remedy.* Bernard Jensen International.

Johnson L Rebecca, Foster Steven, Dog Tieraona (2012*) National Geographic Guide to medicinal herbs: the world's most effective healing plants.* National Geographic Society.

Kessler David, Buff Sheila (1996) *The doctors guide to healing herbs.* Berkley Books.

Kilham Chris (2000) *Tales from the medicine trail*, Rodale Press.

Kloss Jethro (2002) *Back to Eden*, Lotus Press.

Kuenzle Johann (1945) *Das Grosse Kraeuterheilbuch*. Verlag Otta Walter.

Leakey Roger B.(2012) *Living with the Tree of Life*. Cabi.

Linnaeus Carolus (2012*) Species Planetarum* (Latin) General Books.

Lloyd Iva (2009) *The History of Naturopathic Medicine, a Canadian Perspective*. McArthur & Company.

Lust John (1974) *The Herb Book*. Bantam Books.

Lust John, Tierra Michael (1990) *The Natural remedy bible*. Pocket Books.

Matsen Jonn (1998) *The Secrets to great health*, Goodwin Books.

McCaleb R. Leigh E, Morien K (2000) *Encyclopedia of popular herbs: your complete guide to leading medicinal plants*. Prima Publishing.

McKinney, Neil (2010) *Naturopathic Oncology, an Encyclopedia Guide for patients & physicians*, Liaison Press.

McKinney, Neil (2008) *Naturally, there's always hope: healing cancer with natural medicine*. Liaison Press.

Messegue Maurice (1991) *Of people and plants*. Healing Arts Press

Meyer Joseph (1960) *The Herbalist*. Meyerbooks.

Montgomery Pam (2008) *Plant spirit healing: a guide to working with plant consciousness*, Bear & Company.

Mueller Irmgard (1993) *Die pflanzlichen Heilmittel bei Hildegard von Bingen.* Verlag Herder.

Ober C, Sinatra S. Zucker M (2010) *Earthing: the most important health discovery ever?* Basic Health Publication.

Pabst G (1997) *Koehler's Atlas der Medizinal Pflanzen*, Verlag Th. Schaefer.

Rechelbacher Horst (1999) *Aveda Rituals, a daily guide to natural health and beauty.* Henry Holt and Co.

Rona Zoltan (2000) *Natural alternatives to vaccination.* Alive Books.

Schnaubelt Kurt (1999) *Medical Aromatherapy: healing with essential oils.* North Atlantic Books.

Sircus Mark (2004) *Medical Marijuana: treatment of: cancer, radiation exposure, neurological conditions, autism, pain, stress and emotional upset.* IMVA Publications.

St.Claire, Debra (1992) *Pocket Herbal Reference Guide.* Crossing Press.

Suzuki David, Grady Wayne (2004) *Tree – A Life Story.* Greystone Books.

Taylor Leslie (2005) *The healing power of rain forest herbs: a guide to understanding and using herbal medicinals*, Square One Publishing.

Tierra Michael (1993) *The spirit of herbs.* US Games System Inc.

Tierra Michael (1998) *Planetary herbology.* Lout Press.

Tompkins Peter, Bird Christopher (1973)*The Secret of Plants*. Harper Perennial.

Treben Maria (1995) *Health through God's Pharmacy*. Ennsthaler Verlag.

Treben Maria (1987) *Heilkraeuter aus dem Garten Gottes*. Heyne Verlag.

Turner Nancy J. (1998) *Plant Technology of the First Peoples in British Columbia*. UBC Press.

Upton Roy, Graff Allison, Joliff Georgina, Laenger Reinhold Eds. (2011) *American Herbal Pharmacopoea. Botanical Pharmacognosy: Microscopic characterization of botanical medicine*. CRC Press.

Von Bingen Hildegard (1990) *Hildegard von Bingen PHYSICA: The complete English translation of her classic work on health and healing*. Priscilla Throop, Inner Traditions Intl.

Weed Susan.(1989) *Healing Wise – Wise Woman Herbal*. Ash Tree Publishing.

Weil, Andrew (1998) *Natural Health, Natural Medicine*. Houghton Mifflin Company.

Wenzel K.G., Pataracchia RJ (2005) *The Earth's Gift to Medicine*. KOS Publishing.

Whitaker J, Murray M (1996). *Dr. Whitaker's guide to natural healing: leading American wellness doctor shares his secrets for lifelong health*. Harmony.

Willard Terry (2002) *Encyclopedia of Herbs*. Key Porter Books.

Willard Terry (1994) *Textbook of Advanced Herbology*. Wild Rose College of Natural Healing.

Wood Matthew (1997) *The book of herbal wisdom: using plants as medicine*. North Atlantic Books.

Wood Matthew (2008) *The Earthwise herbal: a complete guide to old world medicinal plants*. North Atlantic Books.

Yarnell Eric, Abascall Kathy, Hooper Carol (2003) *Clinical Botanical Medicine*. Mary Ann Liebert Inc

Zevin, Igor Vilevich (1997) *A Russian herbal*. Healing Arts Press.

Suggested Reading:
Healthcare Politics, Prescription drugs, Environment

Abramson John (2004) *Overdo$ed America: How the Pharmaceutical companies are corrupting science, misleading doctors, and threatening your health.* Harper Perennial.

Asthana NC (2001) *The doctor is cheating you: a devastating expose of unethical malpractices in the medicine field.* Author Press.

Bannerman Gary, Nixdorf Don (2005) *Squandering Billions, Health Care in Canada.* Hancock House.

Baker Nena (2009) *The Body Toxic: How hazardous chemistry of everything threatens our health and well being,* North Point Press.

Bavikatte Sandjay Kabir (2004) *Stewarding the Earth: Rethinking property and the emergence of biocultural rights.* Oxford University.

Blech Joerg (2006) *Inventing disease and pushing pills: Pharmaceutical companies and the medicalization of normal life,* Routlage.

Brownstein Art (2005) *Extraordinary Healing, The amazing power of your body's healing secret.* Harbor Press.

Carson Rachel (1962) *Silent Spring.* Houghton Mifflin Harcourt.

Carter James (1992) *Racketeering in Medicine, The Suppression of alternatives.* Hampton Roads Publishing.

Cassels Alan (2007) *ABC of disease mongering, An epidemic in 26 letters.* Emdash Publications.

Cassels Alan (2012) *Seeking Sickness, Medical screening and the misguided hunt for disease.* Grestone Books.

Chopra Shiv (2009) *Corrupt to the Core, Memoirs of a Health Canada Whistle blower.* KOS Publishing.

Colborn Theo (1997) *Our stolen future, Are we threatening our fertility, intelligence and survival?* Plume

Coney Sandra (1994) *The Menopause Industry, How the medical establishment exploits women.* Hunter House.

Conrad Peter (2007) *The Medicalization of Society, On the transformation of human condition into treatable disorders,* The John Hopkins University Press.

Dean Carolyn (2008) *Death by Modern Medicine.* Matrix Verite Inc.

Druker Steven (2015) *Altered Genes, Twisted Truth: how the venture to genetically engineered our food has subverted science, corrupted governments, and systematically deceived the public.* Amazon Digital Services.

Fitzgerald Randall (2007) *The Hundred-Year Lie: How to protect yourself from the chemicals that are destroying your health.* Penguin Group.

Fried Stephen (1998) *Bitter Pills, inside the hazardous world of legal drugs.* Bantam Books.

Peter Gotzsche (2013) *Deadly Medicines and Organised Crime - how big pharma has corrupted healthcare*, CRC Press

Goldacre Ben (2012) *Bad Pharma*, Fourth Estate.

Goozner Merrill (2005) *The $800 Million Pill: The truth behind the cost of new drugs*. University of California Press.

Greider Katherine (2003) *The Big Fix: How the pharmaceutical industry rips off American consumers*, Public Affairs.

Haley Daniel (2000) *Politics in Healing, the suppression and manipulation of American Medicine*. Potomac Valley Press.

Hillary Eve (2009) *Sarah's Last Wish: A chilling glimpse into forced medicine*. Health House.

Hillary Eve (2013) *Beyond Toxic Harvest: A chemical poisoning survivor story, beating the odds, making miracles*. Health House.

Hoffer Abram, Saul Andrew, Hickey Steve (2011) Hospitals *and Health: Your Orthomolecular Guide to a shorter, safer hospital stay*. Basic Health Publication Inc.

Hoffer Abram (2001) *Vitamin & Cancer: discovery, recovery and controversy*. SCB Distributors.

Hollingsworth Elaine (2003) *Doctors are dangerous Take control of your health and escape the sickness industry*. Empowerment Press International.

Holzer Hans (1994) *Healing Beyond Medicine*. Longmeadow Press.

Jacov Alice (2003) *Underground Cures: The Most Urgent Health Secrets*. Health Sciences Institute, Agora Health Books.

Juniper Tony (2013) *What has nature ever done for us? How money really does grow on trees*. Profile Books Ltd.

Kallet A., Schlink F.J (1993) *100,000,000 Guinea Pigs – dangers in everyday foods, drugs and cosmetics*. The Vanguard Press, 1933

Kassirer Jerone (2005) *On the Take: How medicine's complicity with big business can endanger your health*. Oxford University Press.

Kenny Ausubel (1992) *When healing becomes a crime, The suppression of alternatives*. Hampton Road Publishing.

Krishen Pradip (2014) *Jungle Trees of Central India: A field guide for tree spotters*. Penguin.

Kothari Shrivastava & Ashish (2012) *Churning the Earth: The making of Global India*, Penguin Viking.

Lanctot Guylaine (1995) *The Medical Mafia, How doctors serve and fail their customers*. Bridge of Love Publishsing.

Lee John (1999) *What your doctor may not tell you about menopause*. Warner Books.

Leofsky Randall (2000) *Turing illness into growth*. Sunshine Press Publishing.

Mahar Magie (2006) *Money driven medicine*. Collins.

Marcia Angell (2004)*The truth about Drug companies, How they deceive us and what to do about it.* Random House.

McKibben Bill (2006) *The End of Nature, Have we gone too far?* Random House.

Melhorn Heinz. (2011) *Nature Helps: how plants and other organism contribute to solve health problems.* Springer Science & Business.

Mendelsohn Robert (1998) *Confession of a Medical Heretic,* Contemporary Books.

Mendelsohn, Robert (1981) *Male Practice: How doctors manipulate women,* Contemporary Books.

Moynihan Ray, Cassels Allan (2005) *Selling Sickness, How the world's biggest pharmaceutical companies are turning us all into patients.* Greystone Books.

Paul Sharad P. (2003) *Skin Deep, a Biography.* Harper Collins.

Pauling Linus (1986) *How to live longer and feel better.* Oregon State University Press.

Pereira Anand Titus, Pereira Geeta (2009) *Shade Grown Ecofriendly Coffee,* Daijiworld Media.

Pollution Probe Foundation (1994) *Additive Alert: What have they done to our food?* McClelland & Stewart Inc.

Rapp Doris (2004) *Our Toxic World, Chemicals damage your body, brain, behavior and sex.* Environmental Medical Research Foundation.

Richards Byron (2006) *Fight for your health, Exposing the FDA's betrayal of America.* Truth in Wellness.

Roberts, H.J. (1990) *Aspartame (NutraSweet) Is it Safe?* The Charles Press.

Sarjeant Doris Evans Karen (1999) *Hard to Swallow: The truth about food additives.* Alive Books.

Schapiro Mark (2009) *The Toxic Chemistry of everyday products and what's at stake for American power*, Chelsea Green Publishing.

Scheibner, Viera (1993) *Vaccination:100 years of orthodox research shows that vaccines represent an assault on the immune system.* Australian Print Group.

Schlosser Eric (2005) *Fast Food Nation.* Harper Collins.

Shiva, Vandana (1992) *The Violence of the green revolution.* Zed Books.

Shiva, Vandana (1997) *Bio Piracy: The plunder of nature and knowledge.* South End Press.

Shiva, Vandana (1999) *Stolen Harvest: The hijacking of global food supply.* South End Press.

Shiva, Vandana (2002) *Water Wars: Privatization, pollution and profit.* South End Press.

Shiva, Vandana (2006) *Earth Democracy: Justice, sustainable and peace.* South End Press.

Shiva, Vandana (2008) *Soil not Oil: Environmental justice in an age of climate change.* South End Press.

Shiva, Vandana (2012) *Making peace with the Earth: Beyond resource, land and food wars.* South End Press.

Walker Martin (1993) *Dirty Medicine.* Slingshot Publications.

About the Author

Klaus Ferlow, HMH, HA, is a Master Herbalist and manufacturer of botanical health and personal care products. He founded Ferlow Brothers Ltd. in 1975, and the name was later changed to Ferlow Botanicals.

In 1993, he manufactured a wide variety of 'zero harm' herbal products, and the following year he offered herbal Neem products to holistic practitioners in Canada and USA.

After Klaus's retirement in 2013, he appointed his son, Peter, to manage the company and went on to found Neem Research, an organization dedicated to the promotion and preservation of the Neem tree.

His interest in botanicals started in childhood. After his birth in East Prussia, his parents were forced to escape into West Germany during the turmoil of World War II, leaving all behind and narrowly escaping with their lives. As a child, Klaus learned about herbs, when his family used them to heal most minor ailments during a post-war doctor shortage.

 As a young boy, Klaus gathered flowers and herbs from the fields and woods around his home, often selling them to the local villagers.

When Klaus immigrated to Canada with his wife Rose and their two sons in 1975, his herbal knowledge blossomed into a business and became a passionate focus in his life for decades as he supplied botanicals to the North American market.

Over the past 20 years Klaus has also been in demand as an educator, lecturer, researcher and writer in the natural health products industry.

He has been a regular speaker at public health shows in Canada, and lecturer to college students at North American colleges and universities including: College of Naturopathic Medicine in Toronto, The Boucher Institute of Naturopathic Medicine, Canadian Acupuncturist & TCM Alliance, British Columbia Association of Practicing Aromatherapists, Simon Fraser University, Health Action Network Society and Canadian Herbalist's Association of B.C. and National College of Natural Medicine, Portland, Oregon, USA.

His many educational articles about health, healing and herbs were featured in numerous health and women's magazines around the world and on web-sites.

He was interviewed about the healing power of the Neem tree by Peter Mayhew, host of the weekly program 'Human Nature', CHUM radio station. Scott Tips, President of the National Health Federation interviewed him as host of the TSN Radio Station Dublin, Ireland about the healing power of the Neem tree and the hidden dangers lurking in your cosmetics and personal care products. Host Harpreet Singh interviewed Klaus about the miraculous Neem tree at JOY TV Station in Surrey, B.C., Canada. https://plus.google.com/113549744807884498503/post

In 2008, he was only the fourth recipient to receive an Honorary Master Herbalist Diploma (HMH) from Dominion Herbal College in Canada in their 89 year history as North America's oldest school of herbal medicine, for a lifetime of dedication to herbal medicine as promoter and defender of herbs, and the practice of the art and science of herbal medicine.

He is a Board member of the Health Action Network Society, member of the National Health Federation, Neem Foundation, Bombay, International Herb Association, The United Plant Savers and others. He acts as Professional Herbal Advocate (HA) of the Canadian Herbalist's Association of B.C.

He is co-author of the book '7 Steps to Dental Health' and remains a strong advocate for freedom of choice in health care, because he believes: 'Health is wealth'.

Klaus lives with his wife, Rose, in the scenic town of Mission, near Vancouver, Canada, one of the most beautiful harbor cities in the world.

https://www.facebook.com/neemresearch

Praise for the Book

Klaus Ferlow's Book reflects the whole spectrum of benefits of this miraculous medicinal versatile Neem tree from India. Every part of the tree is medicinal: bark, cake, flowers, leaves, oil, timber and roots. The information in the book is easy to read and understand and since it is promoted worldwide every person on the planet has the chance to be educated by reading the book about the benefits this incredible tree offers to mankind. No wonder that it is called in India "The Village Pharmacy." An ancient medicine for a modern world.

--Dr. Joaquim Morgado, M.D, team leader Global Neem Action Group, Mumbai, India

The first comprehensive book on Neem in nearly 20 years covers the latest research from a personal perspective by an author who has been formulating Neem products since 1994. A fabulous resource for anyone thinking about trying or growing Neem including an outstanding list of international growers and manufacturers.

--Vicky Parsons, Neem Tree Farms, Brandon, Florida, USA

Mr. Klaus Ferlow's book "Neem – Nature's Healing Gift to Humanity" is a unique and excellent book for herbal scientists, environmentalists and for all who are interested in nature, Ayurveda and traditional medicine. This book deals with the power of herbs as well as various herbal clinical trials. It highlights the importance of Neem, along with its cosmetic and scientific data and its multiple commercial uses. I can say that the author has tried to cover various facets of this great plant Neem in his book for the benefit of both science and society.

--Professor Dr. Vaidya Suresh Chaturvedi, Mumbai, Ayurveda doctor, lecturer, author of over 25 books, recipient of the Padma Shri award from the Government of India.

During my growing up in India, children used to get all kinds of skin and stomach infections. Back then, antibiotics were not yet invented to prevent such infections. In my own family I was delegated to pluck fresh leaves off a Neem tree, grind them up into a decoction, and let everyone drink half a cup of it, daily, for three weeks. Result: no boils, no diarrhea, and absolutely no side effects! Such is "Nature's Gift to Humanity" offered by Neem. This is the gift of Neem that Klaus Ferlow conveys in his book. Everyone should read it!

--Dr. Shiv Chopra, formerly with Health Canada, Manotick, Ontario, Canada. www.shivchopra.com

Klaus Ferlow is a remarkable scholar, pioneering businessman, teacher, researcher and health care politics advocate and commentator. His substantial knowledge of the Neem plant, coupled with rigorous scholarship and a robust text, he has clearly brought a gift to us which can benefit every botanical medicine professional, as well as their patients and clients.

--Dr. David Schleich, PhD, President & CEO National University of Natural Medicine, Portland, OR, USA

Klaus Ferlow, one of the world's noted western herbalists, has for many years worked passionately to bring knowledge of the many benefits of the miraculous Neem tree from India to the West. His new book relates not only his own fascinating journey but also details the many, many varied Neem applications for personal and planetary healing.

--Katherine Joyce Smith, Editor, The New Zealand Journal of Natural Medicine, Auckland, New Zealand

Klaus Ferlow's book on Neem is a gem. It is a must-read book, enriched with interesting and valuable information about the traditional use of Neem in India. It is well-written and can be easily understood by anyone. The benefits of Neem are well showcased indeed. The compiled information on research institutes, organizations and bibliography is useful ready reckoner for researchers. Congratulations, I enjoyed this one!

--Philipe Haydon, CEO, The Himalaya Drug Company, Bangalore, India

With this book, Klaus Ferlow has created a profound and comprehensive work, one which should be a handbook in every household. This book, with its vivid descriptions of Klaus' own experiences, illustrates the Neem tree's significance for health, and is eminently readable, even for the lay person. It helps every reader find his or her stake in better health. A wealth of medicinal plants are suitable for very different purposes and applications, but none have fascinated us more deeply than the Neem tree, a truly multi-talented medicinal plant. Thank you so much for this excellent book!

--Elke & Stephan Krueger, PlanVerde e.V., Piura, Peru, www.plan-verde.org

A very well written book documenting much detailed data regarding this miraculous tree. It is a must read for all who are interested in Neem, whether their interest lies in agriculture, health & beauty or animal husbandry. The author is very passionate about Neem and this shows very clearly in this excellent publication.

--Brian & Carol William, Directors & Founders, Neeming Australia, Ashmore, Queensland, Australia.

Thank you for this lucid and comprehensive book on Neem. Your scholarship illuminates a brilliant medicine. Neem has been a boon in my clinic practice and my garden.

--Dr. Neil McKinney, ND, BSc., Professor of Naturopathic Oncology, Victoria, B.C. Canada.

A most interesting book illustrating the history and manifold uses for the incredible Neem tree from India. Klaus Ferlow has done a masterful job of detailing the various compounds in this amazing plant and of the ever increasing uses researchers are finding to cure the ailments of both animals and humans. I intend to keep this on my book shelf for its wealth of information, especially the references and Associations contained in the last section of the book.

--Richard DeSylva, RH, DNM, Rockwood, Ontario, Canada.

Neem products are amazing natural tools for returning the chronically ill to excellent health. This book is a well-researched treasure. High praise to Klaus for doing a tremendous job alerting us to the many therapeutic wonders of the Neem tree.
--Zoltan Rona, M.D., M.Sc, Thornhill, Ontario, Canada

The leaves of the Neem tree have long been revered in Ayurvedic medicine for their broad healing properties. Klaus Ferlow describes Neem as "Nature's Healing Gift to Humanity", and his book is a passionate celebration of the extraordinary plant and its various uses – from skin care to digestive support. Ferlow was one of the first to introduce the Indian Neem tree to the West and his book traces his own healing journey using this versatile plant, with an extensive guide to using Neem in your own home.
--Daleen Totten, Editor & Publisher, The South African Journal of Natural Medicine, Die Board, South Africa

The Life of Neem

Named 'Arista' in Sanskrit - meaning 'perfect, complete and imperishable'

Twigs

Whilst used in commercial toothpastes and mouthwashes, twigs have most widely been used as brushes for generations in India

Bark

Neem bark contains spermicidal properties and research is undergoing to approve its potential use as a sexual contraceptive for both women and men

Flowers

The flowers are the part of the tree with fewer uses, however, given the flowers' sweet, honey-like smell, the flowers are used in aromatherapy for a calming and restorative effect

Fruit
Seed
Kernel

Roots

The roots of a neem tree also have different medicinal properties due to being antiseptic, antibacterial, anti fungal and germicidal. They are used as a pesticide and to control fleas and ticks on pets

Leaves

Containing most active ingredients found in the seeds but in a much lower concentration, the leaves are considered the most versatile part of the tree. Now used as a pesticide, fertilizer and animal feed, the leaves were originally used as a medicinal tea in Indonesia

Oil

Extracted from the kernels inside the seeds, where a single seed may contain up to 50% oil by weight, the oil is recognized and valued as a safe and effective bio-pesticide for organic farming. The oil has also been widely studied due to its medicinal properties and is also used in a variety of cosmetic products such as creams, soaps and shampoos

Cake

After the seeds have been pressed for oil, the resulting by-product is the neem cake. Neem cake is used across the agriculture sector as an effective pesticide, fertilizer and anti-bacterial, anti-fungal organic alternative to antibiotics in livestock

Cosmetics

Containing a high level of antioxidants, neem is used in organic soaps, shampoos and hydrating creams

All parts of the neem tree can be used for the treatment of inflammation, infection, fever and other diseases

Neem-based organic pesticides are effective against 600 insect species.

Derived from the